NO OTHER WAY

The Story of a Doctor from East Germany

NO OTHER WAY

The Story of a Doctor from East Germany

———————

HERBERT L. SCHRADER

Translated from the original German by
E. OSERS

DAVID McKAY COMPANY, INC.
New York

NO OTHER WAY

FIRST PUBLISHED IN GREAT BRITAIN 1963
ENGLISH TRANSLATION © GEORGE C. HARRAP & CO. LTD. 1963

FIRST AMERICAN EDITION 1964

LIBRARY OF CONGRESS CATALOG CARD NUMBER: 64–15884

MANUFACTURED IN THE UNITED STATES OF AMERICA

This is the story of a German doctor who lived and worked in Communist East Germany until, in December 1960, he found himself compelled to flee to the West.

Herbert L. Schrader has endeavoured to retell it as factually as possible, without addition or embroidery.

Only the names of the persons involved and the sequence of certain events have been changed so as not to endanger people who are still within the reach of the East German secret police. The names of persons and places are therefore fictitious, and any identity of name with existing persons or places would be purely coincidental.

Part One

1

THE chain of events which were to alter my entire life began on a frosty day in January 1960. It was the day when I met Lola Ried. Every detail of that morning is clearly engraved upon my memory.

I can still see Lola's pale face, with her half-opened mouth. Her titian-coloured wavy hair cascaded down over her cheeks and forehead. Her eyes, with their long lashes, were closed as she lay before me unconscious. She looked like a corpse on the stretcher, with its white blanket. Only a short while before, the ambulance men had pulled her out from the wreckage of her sports car at a level-crossing.

Among the ashen-grey women whom I normally saw around me, she was like some exotic butterfly which had strayed into a backyard and now lay on the ground exhausted, in desperate need of help.

The day had begun quietly enough. I had been on night duty, and was getting ready for my subsequent turn of day duty in the surgical department. In the little pantry opposite my office the water was bubbling on the gas-ring. Through the open window came cool, crisp air. There was a taste of snow in it. For a moment I thought that snow had in fact fallen, for the courtyard and the roofs of the hospital were shimmering in the silver moonlight and under the dim cones of the street lamps. But it was not snow. It was the light dusting of grey ash which every winter settled on the hospital from the chimneys of the boiler-house where unwashed brown coal was fired.

I cursed myself for a fool. If I had not looked so closely I might have preserved my illusion. After all, that was how we were all living in our country at that time—by not looking too closely.

From my briefcase I fished out my sandwiches and the tin of 'Presto' instant coffee. As on every morning, I was faced with the question: one teaspoonful or two? One teaspoonful was not enough to produce a taste of coffee, and two invariably gave me indigestion.

I was about to scoop out the second spoonful when an ambulance siren wailed—from the courtyard. There they go, playing fire brigades again, I grumbled. They might at least shut off their damned horn in the hospital grounds and let the patients get some rest. Angrily I strode across the passage into the pantry and picked up the kettle of boiling water.

But as it happened I had to go without breakfast that morning. Nitschke, the male nurse on duty, rang through from Casualty. The ambulance had brought in an injured woman. It was Lola.

They had set the stretcher down in No. 2 examination room, beneath the portrait of a genially smiling Wilhelm Pieck, re-juvenated by at least twenty years. There was a musty workhouse smell from the damp overcoats of the first patients, who had come early to await the beginning of surgery hours, with their hands bandaged or with patches of adhesive plaster on their faces. The men were bending over the stretcher in a mixture of curiosity and sympathy. "Shame—a pretty young thing like that," a building worker muttered. Nitschke shooed them all out.

Frau Gummer, the Casualty secretary, excitedly pushed her way through to me. She had pulled out an identity card from the patient's crocodile-skin handbag and was thrusting it right into my face. "Her name's Oehmichen," she was whispering. "Could she be the wife of Under-Secretary of State Oehmichen? . . ."

"Surely all that can wait, Frau Gummer," I said.

"If that's who she is it can't wait at all," she hissed. "I'd have to notify Comrade Kranich at once."

I shoved her aside irritably and knelt down by the stretcher. The patient's pulse was rapid and thin. I counted 120 beats. With my forefinger I pulled down her lower eyelids to see if the blood supply in them was normal. She became restless and started babbling incomprehensible words. Nitschke held a kidney-shaped bowl to her mouth.

"What happened to you?" I asked.

The reply came from a long way off: "Don't know . . ."

"What's your name?"

"Lola Ried."

"She's still confused." I could hear Frau Gummer's voice in the background.

"Where d'you live?"

"Berlin."

"And where's the pain?"

"My head . . ." and after a slight groan: "My arm."

There was no doubt about her concussion. The real question was whether there were any complications, such as brain damage. I told her to open her eyes, and looked for any difference in the size of her two pupils. Then, with my hands held close to her eyes, I tried to establish whether her pupils reacted. In a normal person the pupils contract if he is made to look into the bright light of a lamp after his eyes have been shaded for a moment or so by a hand. After concussion, however, it can happen that one of the eyes no longer reacts to the light stimulus. I next examined her to discover whether any blood or cerebrospinal fluid had escaped from her nostrils or ears. Then I felt her head to see whether her skull had been fractured. All these tests, fortunately, proved negative.

When I touched her left forearm the patient screamed. Her arm evidently was broken. While Nitschke turned back the blanket and undid the patient's clothing I started on an examination of her chest and abdomen. The abdomen was rigid—an indication of internal haemorrhage. A slight pressure on the left side of her abdomen produced pain. So the accident had not been quite as harmless as I had hoped at first. The rigidity and the pain suggested a ruptured spleen.

As I straightened up and turned I collided with Frau Gummer's angular elbow. She had remained close behind me, and was still waving the identity card under my nose. There was a hostile look in her little mouse-grey eyes. "Comrade Kranich should be——"

I cut her short: "Comrade Kranich should be nothing. You ring up the radiographer at once. I need an X-ray of her skull, her thorax, and her left forearm."

Muttering under her breath, she went off to the telephone in the next room. But before she lifted the receiver she grumbled: "There'll be trouble, a whole load of trouble."

2

THE operation confirmed our suspicion that the spleen had been ruptured. Purplish, the damaged organ was revealed before us, like a coffee-bean under a magnifying-glass.

A lot of blood had seeped into the abdominal cavity. We had to remove the spleen—extirpate it, as we surgeons say. A ruptured spleen, unfortunately, can never be sewn up because the tissue is too friable. The sutures would simply cut through it. But a person can live quite happily without a spleen.

As I left the operating theatre—the operation had taken about forty-five minutes—two People's Policemen stepped up to me. They had been waiting for me because they needed the medical details for their report. I had a few minutes to spare while the patient was being wheeled to the plaster room. I therefore offered them a *Juwel* cigarette—the only twelve-pfennig ones that are at all smokable, and therefore difficult to get in the shops—and got them to tell me what they knew about the patient and the accident.

The young woman was in fact the wife of Under-Secretary of State Oehmichen, a Communist bigwig from Saxony, newly risen to prominence. She was a well-known dancer, and Lola Ried was her stage name. She had been driving her sports car to one of our winter sports resorts.

Evidently she had dozed off at the wheel. Her car had smashed through a level-crossing barrier, and had been flung aside by a slow train. Fortunately, the train had only just left the main station, and had not been going very fast. The injuries diagnosed by me were in full agreement with the policemen's report. The train had come from the left. That was why the impact had broken her left forearm, and that was also why the spleen, situated as it is on the left side of the body, had been ruptured.

I had to stub out my cigarette before I had finished it, for I suddenly felt a little sick. An extirpated spleen before breakfast is no joke. But there was no time now to think about myself. I had to go down to the plaster room.

On the stairs a voice called out to me from behind: "Excuse me, colleague doctor, one word with you, if you please." It was Paul Kranich, the Political Director of our hospital. On his short, bandy legs he came down two steps at a time. Panting for breath, with beads of perspiration on his flat forehead, he stopped by my side. Short and sallow, badly shaven as always, he was peering at me through the lenses of his State Health Scheme spectacles.

"We must clear a single room at once," he began with a sudden rush. "Just think of it, colleague doctor—the wife of an Under-Secretary! There'll be masses of comrades coming to visit her from Berlin. We've got to show them that the human being is at the centre of all interest here. In our State the human being is the very hub. A bright, cheerful room, flowers on the bedside table, careful attention by Sisters and nurses—that is how we bring our sick people back to health."

We had reached the plaster room. Dr Kukowa and Sister Helga had already started plastering up the arm of our patient, who was still heavily under her anaesthetic. They were using six-inch-wide plaster bandages because we had once again been out of the more convenient narrower ones for several days. Dr Kukowa winked at me and said: "Come to look at the mess?"

Paul Kranich, who was standing behind me in the door, asked irritably: "What's he talking about?"

"The plaster, of course," I replied drily. "The plaster is really very bad," I went on. "It takes ages to set, it crumbles, and weighs three times as much as"—I was about to say 'in the West,' but quickly corrected myself—"as in other countries. A friend of mine at the Foreign Trade Board explained to me a few days ago that the plaster they are sending us here is all frustrated exports—consignments turned down by the purchasing commissions of the importer countries as being of sub-standard quality."

Paul Kranich nervously tugged at the cotton shoelace which he called a tie. "Surely these are not objective difficulties?" he began, in the phony optimistic tone of the Party orator. "In a few months from now everything will be much better."

"In a few months from now the Under-Secretary's wife won't need any plaster of Paris," I pointed out.

He saw the force of my argument. His anger, as a result, was vented on me. "It would have been your duty, dear colleague doctor, to see to it that there is always some good-quality plaster available. For this kind of case—for this kind of serious case," he corrected himself—"some good-quality plaster must be obtained from the West or from the Soviet Union."

Dr Kukowa drew himself up with a great show of indignation. "Surely you're not underrating the plaster capacity of the German Democratic Republic, colleague Kranich?" he said in a tone of voice which always unnerved our Political Director. He just could not make up his mind whether his leg was being pulled or not. With an excuse about urgent cultural work, he hurriedly left the room.

3

However, Paul Kranich's efforts to get a single room for Lola Oehmichen, our V.I.P. patient, had nevertheless run into 'objective difficulties.' The private ward which was normally kept free for such contingencies had been assigned the day before to an official of the Regional Party Executive. As he had just undergone a serious operation, is was not possible to move him. Our patient was therefore accommodated in Ward 16, which already contained five other women.

I had a lot of work that morning, and could not devote too much time to Frau Oehmichen. Because of the acute shortage of doctors in East Germany, every *Oberarzt* like myself—I suppose in England we should be known as Senior Registrars—was responsible for his own ward or group of wards. I therefore instructed my most reliable Sister, Eva Schirmer, to look after our important patient, who was still sleeping.

Sister Eva, pale, thin, and very tall, was a quiet and reserved girl. Both her parents had been killed one night in an air raid, when she was not yet five. She had grown up in an orphanage, and had been brought up strictly in the new official faith. The result of this upbringing, however, was not so much a fanatical love for the State and the Party as large gaps in her education and serious blank spaces in her nursing knowledge. But what she lacked in knowledge she made up for in keenness and efficiency.

Shortly after lunch Sister Eva reported that the patient had woken up. She had opened her eyes and asked for water, which the Sister, of course, was not yet allowed to give her. By the time I got to her bed she had fallen asleep again.

I withdrew to my office with a stack of case-histories. The only time we doctors had for catching up with our daily paper work was the lunch-break. Presently the Hospital Director's secretary rang through to ask when the Director, Professor Brunke, could call on Frau Oehmichen. I said in two hours at the earliest; before then the patient was unlikely to take much notice.

About an hour later the door of my office was opened softly. Dr Kukowa crept in, a suppressed smile playing around the corners of his mouth and his eyes. "The great performance is about to begin," he whispered, pointing to the window.

I got up from my chair and looked out. Across the courtyard, striding purposefully and with great dignity, came Professor Dr Eberhard Brunke, Director of the hospital as well as chief of the medical department. He was an impressive figure—tall, slim, his grey hair carefully brushed. Even in the faded railwayman's jacket and shabby corduroy trousers that he was wearing, he still looked like an aristocrat in disguise. In his left hand he was nonchalantly carrying a spade: he was determined to do a 'voluntary reconstruction shift.'

To us the only new feature in this scene was his corduroy trousers. In the past he had always set out on his noble patriotic enterprise in a freshly pressed pair of consultant's pin-striped. Professor Brunke was a physician of the old school, with a good university education. In the old days it had been his ambition to be appointed to a teaching post. Now he wanted at least to become a Meritorious People's Doctor.

Behind the boiler-house was a plot which was still covered with rubble and wrecked masonry from the War. According to the plans, an extension to the hospital was to be built there at some future date. This plot had been selected by the Director for his voluntary reconstruction shifts. The whole hospital staff were marched out by Paul Kranich, the Political Director, at more or less regular intervals to do their voluntary reconstruction shifts somewhere among the ruins of the neighbourhood. But Professor Brunke performed his solitary additional shifts in full view of most of the hospital windows. The moment his spade struck the broken masonry and the first spadeful of stones clattered into a conveniently placed wheelbarrow all work would cease throughout the building. Heads would appear in all the windows. Indeed, some two hundred man-hours might have been lost to the hospital if the Director had really put in a full hour's work with his spade. Fortunately, the hospital was never to suffer such a loss. The Director's special shift, begun with such a fine flourish of goodwill, invariably ended within ten minutes. There was always some unforeseen circumstance to tear him away from his patriotic effort. As a rule, this circumstance appeared in the shape of his secretary, who arrived on the scene to call the Director to some urgent official business.

And the spectators behind the windows were now really only waiting for that climax when the secretary would make her dramatic entrance with the important message for the Director.

"Eleven minutes—eleven minutes, thirty seconds—if he goes on like this he'll be made a Meritorious People's Doctor before our very eyes," Dr Kukowa prophesied at my side, his glance alternating between his wristwatch and the Director's busy spade.

Professor Brunke was no Communist, but he acted as if he were one. He was far too shrewd to join the Party. His nickname in the hospital was 'Radish'—because he was red on the outside but white inside. So white, in fact, that he could easily have continued his career under any other regime.

Thirteen minutes, thirty seconds. Suddenly Kukowa gave a little shout. "Look—I'm seeing things. They're really going to make him a Meritorious People's Doctor!"

From the administrative block came Brunke's secretary, with a white coat over her left arm, and in her right hand a bunch of flowers. Taking short, mincing steps beside her, and looking important, was Paul Kranich.

"This is the greatest moment of my life," Kukowa said, in the tone of voice which always unnerved Paul Kranich. "My supreme and revered chief is about to be made a Meritorious People's Doctor and have his bank account increased annually by 15,000 Deutsche Mark."[1]

But Kukowa's ideas on the presentation of this honourable title were clearly a little too naïve. The dramatic climax of the well-known performance was to take an entirely different turn. The angry frown into which the Director was wont to compose his forehead whenever his secretary arrived to interrupt his peaceful reconstruction work was smoothed out. And there was no solemn address by the Political Director. Professor Brunke merely thrust

[1] The fundamental difference in the economic structure of a Communist country, together with the fact that rationing and price control continue to exist in various fields in East Germany, makes it impossible to give reliable equivalents for salaries, wages, and prices mentioned in this book. The official Year Book of the German Democratic Republic for 1961 gives the average earnings of an industrial worker in 1960 as 567 East German Deutsche Mark per month. By Government decree of October 29, 1953, the value of the East German Deutsche Mark was laid down as 2·22 DM = 1 U.S. dollar, or 1·80 DM = 1 rouble. According to an authoritative West German publication (Bonn, 1959), these equivalents are meaningless, since East German currency is not freely convertible. Unofficially, but quite openly, East German Deutsche Mark have been obtainable in West Berlin for several years at a rate of 4 East German Deutsche Mark for 1 West German Deutsche Mark.—Translator's Note.

his spade into the rubble, with a sigh that was almost audible from where we were watching, allowed his secretary to help him on with his white coat, and followed the two interrupters of his peaceful reconstruction work towards the surgical block.

Kukowa and I exchanged startled glances. If the flowers in the secretary's hand were not intended for the peaceful reconstruction worker among the ruins, then surely they must be for our patient Frau Oehmichen? It would be a kindness to her, drowsy as she still was after her anaesthetic, to prepare her for what was coming. We walked over to her bed, where Sister Eva was still keeping watch.

Lola Oehmichen had opened her eyes, but she was feeling very sorry for herself, and irritable. Admittedly she was in an uncomfortable position, but that was what the medical requirements demanded in her case. We had laid her entirely flat, without a pillow. Her wavy hair flowed out from underneath the ice-pack. Her left arm, in plaster, was held in position on a stand.

From the loudspeakers came noisy music. These loudspeakers were installed in every ward, and were a sore trial for the seriously ill. The installation was centrally controlled, and the individual loudspeakers could not be disconnected. This radio irrigation with music and propaganda was part of Paul Kranich's 'cultural programme.'

The door was gently opened. Professor Dr Brunke, the aristocrat in the white coat, stepped in. Behind him, fidgety and untidy, appeared the thin figure of Paul Kranich.

Brunke bent down as if to kiss Lola's hand, but evidently remembered just in time that hand-kissing was a survival from the bourgeois era. So instead he treated the still apathetic patient to a flow of well-chosen words. He expressed his pleasure at finding her looking so well, assured her that it was a privilege for him to make her acquaintance, even though through a tragic turn of fate. He was proud, he said, to be the Director of one of the most progressive hospitals. He could confidently entrust her to my care, and was convinced that she would feel happy among us as soon as the first trying days after her operation were over.

Needless to say, he did not omit to ask her indulgence for his plain working trousers underneath his white coat, although, of course, lying flat as she was, she could not have seen them anyway. But this reference enabled him to mention the voluntary reconstruction shift which he had just performed.

Paul Kranich used a momentary lull in the conversation to push his way past the obsequious back of the Hospital Director and offer his own services. "If you have any cultural requirements, Frau Oehmichen," he bleated, "please do not hesitate to turn to me, the Political Director. Newspapers, brochures, propaganda leaflets, documents about our peaceful struggle—we have everything here."

For the first time I noticed a mocking smile about the corners of Lola's mouth. "You think they will help me to get well?" she asked in a drawl.

Paul Kranich wriggled his head another half-inch out of his grubby collar. He felt flattered by the question. "Yes, indeed. Participation in cultural achievements and faith in progress are important factors in convalescence," he replied.

Professor Brunke had clearly noticed by now that the patient was not yet ready for this kind of conversation. The lack of tact of the insensitive Party man irritated him. Moreover, he seemed to feel ashamed that as an intellectual with a university education he had to appear side by side with that type of man. He soon found some pretext for terminating the visit.

When I entered the ward again in the evening, shortly before going off duty, Lola Ried was lying with her eyes shut. Sister Eva showed me the chart on which she had entered the patient's pulse at hourly intervals. The post-operative pattern was so far satisfactory. While I was talking to Sister Eva the patient opened her eyes. It was only then that I saw that they were emerald green and of quite unbelievable luminosity. They looked out of the pale face with that mixture of helplessness and astonishment that I had previously known only in the eyes of children.

4

I WAS tired and spent when I got home that evening. I had been thirty-six hours on duty. We occupied two attic rooms in a tenement block dating back to before the first war. My wife was pottering about in the kitchen, pale and careworn. She received me with an account of the worries which had spoilt her day. She had tried in vain to find any cheese in the State-owned food shops of our district. As if to make up for this shortage, there was plenty of butter available, which only a few months earlier had been unobtainable. She had stood in a queue for an hour to get some vegetables, and all she had got in the end was a few frostbitten carrots.

Night after night she would unload the same irritation upon me. It was quite true that for some years now nobody need starve any longer in our country, but it still was not worth while for a housewife to plan what she was going to give her family for lunch or supper. She simply had to see what there was in the shops. If the butcher had any fresh beef there would almost certainly be no onions; if she got a leg of pork from the butcher, then there would be no sauerkraut; and if by any chance the baker had some rye-bread, then there would be no cheese at the grocer's. As a man I was not unduly worried by all this. I should have been quite prepared to eat rye-bread with salted herrings if only my wife had looked more cheerful. But I am enough of a psychologist to understand that this kind of continuous breakdown in our planned economy is a heavy trial for our womenfolk.

Because I was too tired to think of some pleasant remark to comfort her, her anger was vented on me. "We could have been in the West long ago if only you had more courage. A letter came from Gerd to-day. He has just opened a practice in Bavaria. He's barely been out three months, and he's managed it already."

Dr Gerd Reger had been a junior doctor at our hospital. We

were friends, even though he was nearly ten years younger than I. Naturally, my wife and I had often considered the possibility of going to the West—after all, who does not consider it from time to time in our country?—but I doubt if Gerd Reger would have left entirely of his free will.

Gerd had been rather foolish one night. After a somewhat lively drinking party at the Ratskeller with some young colleagues, they had walked home through the streets and, being a bit tipsy, they had intoned an old song: "We want our Kaiser Wilhelm back." A People's Policeman had stopped them, but when all three of them identified themselves as doctors he had merely told them to pull themselves together and go home and sleep it off. I don't know what possessed Gerd to do what he did. Instead of going home to bed and being grateful to the policeman—who after all had run a certain risk himself in deciding not to report them—he began to insult him. Naturally enough, the man took Gerd's name and address.

The following morning a black Sachsenring saloon pulled up outside the entrance to the surgical department. Several well-dressed but hatless gentlemen got out and asked the young woman in Reception where they could find Dr Gerd Reger. Hatless men arriving in black Sachsenring saloons—every child in East Germany knows that they are the secret police. The girl in Reception did some quick thinking, sent the men to a wrong ward, and hurriedly rang through to Gerd. He scuttled down the back stairs, slipped out of the building, and took the train to Berlin.

In his case, therefore, not a great deal of courage was needed for the decision to go over to the West.

"Have you spoken to the District Medical Officer about a flat?" my wife asked abruptly.

I lied that he would be coming to the hospital the next day. In actual fact I had completely forgotten about him during my work.

Our conversation that evening remained rather monosyllabic. We were both irritable. A single spark might have set off an explosion.

"Look, Ruth," I said, after many long silences. "If conditions here become really quite unbearable, then we'll go. But at this moment I couldn't even if I wanted to. To-day I had to operate on a prominent patient. It'll be three days at least before I know that she is all right. At this critical stage I could not possibly leave her to Kukowa."

"And who is this celebrity?"

"Lola Ried, the wife of Under-Secretary of State Oehmichen."

"And she's impressed you so much?" Ruth asked cattily. "So much that you've got to stay here for her sake?"

"She is my patient," I replied firmly.

Ruth said nothing.

5

THE next morning Lola received me in high spirits. Her emerald-green eyes were twinkling when I came to look at her during my round. She had combed her hair, and was spreading an aura of French perfume. I was surprised and delighted that she should feel the urge to groom herself so soon after the operation. From the medical point of view, this could only mean that there were no complications. A glance at the pulse chart held ready by Sister Eva confirmed this impression. The previous evening I had feared that her pulse might slow down during the night. That might have indicated a cerebral haemorrhage—a much-feared complication after severe concussion.

I asked Lola if she was in pain. The fact that her head and body ached was not in the least alarming.

"Giddiness?" Yes, she had felt giddy once or twice. But, surprisingly enough, she seemed quite ready for a joke. "But then, Doctor, a woman likes living giddily occasionally—and all your pills can't stop it." From the loudspeaker came a lilting tune from *The Merry Widow*.

After such convincing evidence of her progress I had no hesitation in breaking to her the glad tidings that a Russian Zis limousine accompanied by two black Sachsenring saloons was standing outside the hospital. A delegation from the Ministry, escorted by hatless gentlemen of the State Security police, had come to pay a visit to the wife of the Under-Secretary of State. The gentlemen had been waiting for me in Reception. I had told them that only after my round would I be able to say whether Frau Oehmichen's condition permitted of a visit that day.

Lola seemed neither surprised nor particularly delighted. "And when shall I see you again, Doctor?" she asked.

"This afternoon. Unless you cause me some anxiety before then."

She laughed roguishly. "Don't worry, I'll cause you a lot of anxiety yet."

A groan from the next bed reminded me that it was time to continue my round. Frau Novotny, a woman of sixty-eight, who was accustomed to being the first in the ward to be examined by me on my round, was in this way drawing attention to herself. She was our 'regular' patient, and had been in that bed, and in pain, for some six months. We all pampered her a little because she was a tragic victim of our outdated hospital equipment.

"Well, Granny Novotny, and how are you to-day?" I asked.

"Much the same as usual, Herr Doktor," she complained. "Always in pain. And those tablets don't do me any good any more."

Granny Novotny was a refugee from the Sudetenland. About six months ago she had broken her hip—or, to be exact, the neck of her femur. Because the bones of elderly people do not easily knit together, we decided to insert a pin. This means that a laminated pin is driven into the head of the femur—the bone of the thigh—from the outside. It is so driven forward inside the bone that the two broken pieces are firmly held to each other. Now, to make sure that the two pieces of bone are in the correct position during the insertion of the pin, two X-ray machines are used. We had positioned one of these underneath the fracture and the other between the patient's legs, so that we could take pictures in two planes. The X-ray machine between the patient's legs was covered with sterile towels. Both machines were operated by our very reliable radiographer. And both of them were switched off in accordance with the correct drill.

A few days afterwards we noticed to our horror that the patient's thigh showed severe X-ray burns over an area about eight inches wide. Throughout the lengthy operation one of the machines had been emitting X-rays although it had been switched off. Examination showed that the switch of the machine—an X-ray veteran of 1940 vintage—had suddenly packed up. Since the tube had been covered with towels, nobody had noticed that it was still on.

Since then Granny Novotny had been in severe pain as a result of continuing destruction of the tissue. We often gave her morphine—whenever the pain became unbearable. A theatre nurse, who had been standing near by and had likewise suffered radiation damage, had some healthy skin grafted on her injuries, but poor Frau Novotny was still faced with the prospect of hospital for an uncertain period of time. That was why we regarded her as the 'regular' of Ward 16. The fact that we had put her in a six-bed ward instead of one of the general wards with fourteen to thirty beds was one of the few privileges which we were in a position to grant her.

As for the other occupants of the ward, there was a fairly rapid turnover. Opposite Granny Novotny was a young girl from the country with a broken leg which was mending satisfactorily. Next to her was a schoolgirl who had had her appendix out, and over by the window was a textile-mill worker who had had her gall bladder removed. They were none of them complaining of pain that morning.

I therefore turned to Frau Steinkopf, whose bed was by the window opposite the woman without the gall bladder, and next to Lola. Ilse Steinkopf was an energetic woman of forty-five, the wife of a master locksmith who still ran his own business, and the mother of three children. She was invariably cheerful, and positively radiated a kind of infectious gaiety. I believe that she was one of the last surviving representatives of this type of woman in our town. Her optimism came from the heart, and did not need nourishing by the watery slogans of our Party people.

"Well, then, Frau Steinkopf," I said to her, "to-morrow we are having that stomach ulcer of yours out."

She laughed broadly, revealing a row of strong white teeth. "Boy, oh boy, once I've got rid of that swine I'm going to give a party that'll make the town rock."

Even the fact that she was given no food that day did not seem to affect her cheerfulness.

I quickly terminated my round and notified the delegation from Berlin that they could visit Lola Oehmichen. It was getting time for me to start on my list of operations.

6

To GET from the wards of the surgical department to the operating theatre I had to cross the hospital courtyard. Two men of the outdoor staff, wearing blue overalls, put a large basket full of potatoes down in front of me. One of them, a tall, strong giant with a thatch of fair hair and the face of a simpleton, addressed me. He was Ernst Pfeifer, a typical example of the working-class youth who supports communism because it promises him a social position which he could never achieve by his own efforts.

"Herr Oberarzt," he said awkwardly, "I should like to qualify and become an assistant nurse."

Qualify—that has become the great magic formula in our country for vocational advancement by means of special courses and high-pressure classes. Because of the universal shortage of qualified labour, the Party is appealing to the young people to qualify—that is, to acquire special knowledge and skill with State support. The incentive, of course, is the prospect of higher pay.

From what I knew of Ernst Pfeifer, he had displayed neither particular application nor conscientiousness during his employment on the outdoor staff. His intelligence, too, seemed to me to be well below the educational level of even quite ordinary people. I did not raise any great hopes, but told him I would speak to Matron.

We had three operations that morning. Afterwards, as I was going to see my chief to report to him about them, I found that fate itself had decided to exonerate me from my white lie of the previous evening. For in the door to the administration office I collided with our District Medical Officer, Dr Schwiers. He was a man in his fifties, with steel-grey hair and a nervously twitching face which reflected vagueness and lack of concentration. I decided to seize the opportunity and tackle him about the flat I had been promised. He looked at me absent-mindedly, chewed his stub of a cigar, and mechanically switched on his professional patter of vague promises. I knew at once that he would promise anything to anybody and forget about it again the very next moment. I could see that he had no intention of making a nuisance of himself to his superiors merely to press the justified demands of the doctors under his administration.

Such, then, was our conversation in the doorway. To whatever I said the District Medical Officer nodded vigorously. Indeed—of course—I was entitled to a flat, and he would do everything in his power; I should certainly hear from him within the next few days, and I could rely on him entirely. And off he went.

My chief, Professor Zöllinger, the head of the surgical department, listened to my account of the operations with only half an ear. His tanned leathery skin indicated the former athlete. He was entirely taken up by his scientific work, and took little interest in the day-to-day running of the hospital. As for the authorities and the Party, he avoided them wherever possible. He was able to do this because his colleague, Professor Brunke, was not only head of the medical department, but at the same time Director of the hospital as a whole.

Whenever Professor Zöllinger had organizational worries he simply unloaded them on to me. To-day was no exception. "The district M.O. has asked me to keep two private wards ready as from to-morrow because a foreign Head of State is visiting the town."

"The Head of State is ill?" I asked.

"No, he's sound as a bell." When he had amused himself long enough looking at my uncomprehending face he continued: "But no matter how sound a man is he may very suddenly find himself a patient—for instance, through the bullet of some enemy of the State. But this, of course, is my own private interpretation."

At any rate, I was to see to it now that by to-morrow morning enough patients were discharged, regardless of whether this was medically advisable or not. Certainly this put an end to any attempt to get a private ward for Lola. Of all the V.I.P.s who from time to time enjoyed that privilege, I would have most gladly granted it to her.

But that was not the chief's only worry. "What d'you think is the trouble with Hansen?" he asked. "I am told he left the hospital yesterday as early as 11 a.m. There's constantly some complaint or other about him."

Dr Hansen, a junior doctor, was in charge of one of my four wards. He was unreliable and unconscientious. He turned up for duty whenever it suited him. In the afternoon he was frequently seen in bars, drinking beer. He would stand at the operating table sleepy, and with a hangover. His duties in the ward he simply passed on to a young houseman, the one we called the 'living corpse,' because of his pale and emaciated appearance. We should have long ago dismissed Hansen if he had not got the backing of the Party and the trade-union movement, which he had joined, and where he had risen to the post of chairman of our B.G.L., our local trade-union committee. The chief now ordered me to have a serious talk with him, and to threaten disciplinary measures un-less he changed his mode of life. How nice it must be to be a *Chefarzt*,[2] I thought to myself. Then one can just palm off all the unpleasant tasks on to one's *Oberarzt*.[3]

2 Chief of Staff.
3 Senior medical officer.

7

I HAD been secretly looking forward to my afternoon round. I was disappointed. Nearly a dozen men were sitting round Lola, on chairs and on the edges of beds. A new delegation had arrived, this time from the Central Committee of the Party. Lola's bedside table, as well as a small occasional table which had been specially brought in, looked like the display counter of some luxury delicatessen shop. Bananas and oranges, chocolate, marzipan, bottles of Tokay and Crimean champagne, tins of caviare and *pâté de foie gras*, large boxes of glacé fruits and chocolates with liqueur centres were piled high on top of each other. For the most part, judging by the brand names, they were made in West Germany.

The gentlemen from the Central Committee moved apart to make room for me. Lola with great presence of mind seized on the moment of the chairs scraping on the floor to glance around and say: "I am very grateful to you, comrades, for looking after me so well." The comrades understood and rose. Paul Kranich, who was escorting them, gave my sleeve a tug and motioned me to step outside into the corridor. I interrupted my round.

Outside the gentlemen wished to know how I judged Lola's prospects of recovery, and whether any further complications were to be expected. While we were slowly strolling down the passage I assured them that I expected a normal course of recovery. A man with an energetic chin and a scar on his forehead asked me: "Do you need any special medicines for Frau Oehmichen, Herr Doktor? We could easily get them for you from the dispensary at the Government Polyclinic in Berlin and have them sent down by special courier." As a matter of fact, the same offer had been made to me that morning by the delegation from the Ministry. I knew, of course, that the dispensary at the Government Polyclinic in Berlin stocked all kinds of pharmaceutical treasures from all over the world—preparations which we doctors in hospitals for the non-privileged population knew of only from the medical periodicals. For Lola's treatment, however, the currently available medicines were quite adequate. I declined the offer with thanks and was about to take my leave.

But just then Paul Kranich pointed with a dramatic gesture to a niche in the corridor. There he had set up a 'peace corner,' as prescribed for all hospitals and all other enterprises. As a special measure in honour of the afternoon's visit he had filled the vases on the little table with hothouse carnations, which were very expensive just then in winter. The 'peace corner' consisted of a table covered with red cloth, behind which was a blue wall-hanging. On the table were propaganda leaflets, to be picked up by those passing by, and a book bound in cardboard into which every member of the staff was supposed to enter his voluntary pledges. From a sheet of white cardboard Paul Kranich had cut out a Picasso peace dove and some letters spelling out a Party slogan, and had fastened them all with pins to the dark wall-hanging.

"There, comrades," Paul Kranich intoned, "this is the pride of our hospital. If you care to glance into our book of voluntary pledges you will be surprised. What's more, I have a special surprise for you to-day." From his coat pocket he pulled out a crumpled copy of the Party newspaper and pointed to a passage which he had marked in red crayon. "We are going to set up the first socialist brigade in our hospital. Look—it says so here."

But the comrade with the energetic chin and the cigar was not looking at the paper. He was staring fascinated at the slogan on the wall. Slowly his face turned the colour of burgundy. I followed his glance, and only just managed to stop myself from bursting out laughing. I dug my teeth into my lips and looked again. And there, in large white letters on a blue background, was the slogan which, translated into English, read: 'The serfdom of the working people ensures the victorious building of socialism' (*Die Fron der Werktätigen ist der Garant für den siegreichen Aufbau des Sozialismus*).

A storm of indignation broke out. The comrades pounced upon Paul Kranich, who a moment before had been so puffed up with pride. He ducked and cringed under their vituperation. In fact, he literally went down on his knees, stretched out his arms under the red tablecloth which hung down to the floor, and fished about for

27

a grubby piece of cardboard. The piece was in the shape of a small cross, and Paul was holding it up towards the excited comrades, like a sinner trying to defend himself against an army of devils. Then he picked up a pin and put the small letter 't' back in the place from which it had so maliciously vanished. And now at last the slogan ran as Paul had intended it to run: 'The serried ranks of the working people ensure the victorious building of socialism' (*Die Front der Werktätigen ist der Garant für den siegreichen Aufbau des Sozialismus*). But the wrath of the comrades was not to be allayed as easily as that. The grubby little 't' stood out among the other letters like an unruly black sheep among a flock of white ones. It was standing in the way of truth.

8

LOLA was delighted with her treasures. While I examined her the radio was playing popular music from the Bohemian frontier area. Lola was chattering excitedly like a child who had been showered with presents. What delightful people those men from Berlin were! True, some were a little simple, or dogmatic, or philistine—but they were all very decent chaps at heart. The moment she was well again she would take me along and introduce me to her friends. "There are only very few Party officials among my friends. Those Party people are always so serious and learned, and they will talk about things of which I understand nothing. Most of them are as dry and matter-of-fact as my husband. Of course, we've got to be grateful to them for liberating us and for leading us along the road to socialism, as they call it. But as a woman they just bore me."

"You don't look like a woman who is often bored," I said. She winked at me roguishly. "I'll tell you my secret, Doctor. There are a lot of things in life which we just have to submit to. This radio here in hospital, for instance. We patients can't turn it off.

But you can train yourself not to listen to it. No matter how loud it blares—I don't let it penetrate into my world. But I'm talking nonsense, Doctor—a sign that I'm getting well again."

She had no idea how her words fascinated me. This brief glimpse of her simple philosophy made her even more attractive to me. I should have kissed her hand if we had been alone.

I suddenly noticed that Sister Eva, who was near the head of the bed, was looking much paler than usual. I asked her whether looking after Frau Oehmichen had been very tiring—and tears promptly began to run down her cheeks. Could it be that she was jealous? A woman's tears always confuse me. I asked her to come outside with me. On my way to the door I intercepted Granny Novotny's greedy glance towards the delicacies piled high by Lola's bed. Evidently Lola had not yet offered her any of her treasures.

There was no one in the pantry, so I sat down there with Sister Eva. But at first my searching questions produced nothing but tears. Then abruptly she straightened up, that pale slip of a girl, and exclaimed: "If you really must know, Herr Oberarzt—I'm going to have a baby."

She was shaken by a renewed fit of sobbing, and hid her face in her hands. I promised I would help her.

"No," she screamed, and with her arm pushed me aside. "I want to keep the child. All you're thinking of is the gossip. Of course there'll be gossip; there always is when anything happens at the hospital."

"I had a different kind of help in mind, Sister Eva," I corrected the misunderstanding. "Have you told the father?"

She shook her head violently.

"Do you want to tell me who he is?"

Again she shook her head frantically, and produced another flood of tears.

"In that case I honestly don't see how I can help you."

Still sobbing, she admitted: "I think it was Ernst Pfeifer."

"The one on the outdoor staff?"

She nodded.

"And, my dear girl, you only think it is him?"

"It could be Dr Hansen."

My brain reeled. "Perhaps it could be someone else still?" I asked.

"No, I don't think so," she replied, in a matter-of-fact voice.

This, then, I thought, was the result of our much-vaunted new Communist morality. And I had always regarded Sister Eva as quiet and reserved—at least, that was the impression she gave in the hospital.

A nurse entered the pantry with a tray full of dirty crockery. This interruption made it easy for me to cut short our conversation. After these startling revelations I should have found it difficult to think of some way of helping Sister Eva.

9

ON THE main staircase I ran into Matron. At first, after my conversation with Ernst Pfeifer, that blond moron, I had felt very little inclination to pass on to Matron his request to be allowed to qualify as an assistant nurse. But it now occurred to me that this might be a way of helping Sister Eva.

Matron, whose name was Margot Kress, stopped and turned to me. Her large, hungry eyes and her dark, naturally wavy hair contrasted strangely with her severe uniform. She was only just past forty, full-breasted and temperamental. Her love affairs were a never-ending source of gossip throughout the hospital. When I started to talk to her about Pfeifer's request she stopped me with a wave of her hand. "I know all about it. Comrade Kranich submitted the matter to me this morning with his own recommendation. No doubt Comrade Pfeifer asked Comrade Kranich to sponsor his application at the same time as he asked you. I have already agreed."

That had not been a bad move on Ernst Pfeifer's part. Certainly I could not have supported his application as warmly as had Paul Kranich—at least, not with a good conscience.

Towards evening, just as I was on my way to my office, I remembered that I had to talk to Hansen. Dr Hansen, the possible father of Sister Eva's child. I was not looking forward at all to our meeting; the only cheering thought about it was my certain belief that Hansen would no longer be in the hospital at this time of day. But miracles sometimes happen. He was already sitting in my office, waiting for me. The chief's secretary, he said, had told him of the thundercloud that had been gathering over his head.

There he stood before me: tall, slim, but his face weak and dissolute. His dark hair was razor-cut in the American fashion—a trick which only a few hairdressers had learnt in our country as yet.

He wanted to start our conversation with a few polite phrases, but I cut him short. I was his superior, and I was responsible for whatever happened in his ward and during his operations. All the things that had been annoying and irritating me about him during the past few weeks I now flung in his face. I reminded him that in our job there were always human lives at stake, and that any neglect of duty might have far more serious consequences than in any other walk of life. Unless he mended his ways I should be obliged to ask for a disciplinary transfer for him. But the more sharply I spoke to him the more provocative became his smile.

"Herr Oberarzt," he said, with a suggestion of menace in his voice; "Herr Oberarzt, you know very well that I have more work to do than you. My position as chairman of the trade-union committee and my work as the principal medical officer of the People's Police here demand a great deal of my time and some consideration from you. The trade-union committee too is concerned with human beings—the human beings which make up our hospital. We too have to take decisions—decisions which sometimes are far more important than those of an *Oberarzt*. I beg your pardon; I did not mean to be personal."

"I am not talking now to the chairman of the trade-union committee, Herr Hansen, but to the doctor responsible for No. 3 Ward. And as your superior I am sorry to have to inform you that you are discharging your duties in a very inadequate way."

Hansen regarded me challengingly. "Surely you do not wish to

31

continue your life as an *Oberarzt*, Herr Oberarzt. Therefore you ought to be more just towards your subordinates. I could help you to get a *Chefarzt* position very quickly. I have good connexions with the Party and with a number of State authorities. I often have a drink or two with the District Medical Officer. As for my work in the hospital, I freely admit that during the past few weeks it has suffered a little owing to the heavy burden of other important official business that I had to bear. But I promise you that I shall make every effort in the future to discharge my duties in the hospital to your satisfaction."

I felt a strong temptation to spit into that depraved face. The man's impertinent offer to use his influence in my favour infuriated me. But I had no further justification for continuing my complaints. He had given me his assurance that he would do his duty properly in the future. It was simply this assurance that my chief had asked me to exact from him.

We parted with frosty smiles. I had an uncomfortable feeling—a feeling I remembered from my childhood when I had failed to beat up a younger and apparently weaker boy simply because he knew some tricks which I did not know. But neither of us had a sufficiently strong starting position for a major clash. So the best thing was probably just to keep out of one another's way.

I remained sitting at my desk for a long time, lost in thought. To keep out of a subordinate's way who was neglecting his duty and jeopardizing human lives—that was plain cowardice. Moreover, it was a criminal offence. But in our country it was sometimes wiser to break a conventional law than to fall foul of the rules of the Party. These were not healthy thoughts to entertain—after all, they had been nagging at us these past fifteen years, and we had tried to live with them. But by living with these thoughts we are harming not our tormentors but ourselves. In the long run a man cannot live with bitterness in his heart and in his mind, and with a persistent bitter taste in his mouth.

Lola had made a very clever remark, a remark which summed up something that most of us have long accepted as our everyday philosophy without clearly realizing it. "No matter how loud the radio blares—I don't let it penetrate into my world." This, I believe, is the only recipe for making life bearable in East Germany to-day. We are powerless against the blaring radio, and we cannot switch it off ourselves. But we do get used to not listening to it, and to keeping our own private little worlds intact. Every person for himself, or a few like-minded persons together. These are not things that it is wise to discuss in company, but we do not need words to understand one another, and we sense clearly that we represent many millions.

That night I made a resolution to live even more strictly in accordance with this principle, a principle of which I had not until then been fully conscious. It was probably the only way of preserving one's substance as a human being in the circumstances in which we were living.

10

WHEN I made my round on the following morning the bed next to Lola's was empty. The ever-cheerful Frau Steinkopf, the first on our list of operations that morning, had already been taken to the anaesthetics room.

Lola complained of a headache, and was obviously depressed. The orange she was munching seemed bitter to her.

"Would you like a liqueur chocolate, Doctor?" she asked me. In spite of the plaster on her left arm, she could now move well enough to reach all her treasures on the bedside table with her right hand. "Where are the liqueur chocolates?" she suddenly screamed. She looked reproachfully at Sister Eva. We pulled the bedside table away, we shone a torch under her bed, but the box which I had myself seen the previous day was gone. A moment later Sister Eva was pulling it out from underneath Granny Novotny's pillow. It was nearly empty. Perplexed, we looked at the old woman, who was sobbing hysterically and hiding her face in her pillow.

"You're making me share a room with thieves and robbers!" Lola shrieked. "Go and call the police at once, Doctor."

Instead I sat down on the edge of Granny Novotny's bed. I had known her for some six months, and had never noticed in her any tendency to steal. I had to talk to her for a long time before she would tell me, still amid tears, how she had become a thief. The previous afternoon Lola had invited Frau Steinkopf to help herself to some of her delicacies. Frau Steinkopf, with a very heavy heart, had to decline because she was on strict starvation prior to her operation. Lola in her innocence had assumed that her other roommates were likewise forbidden to have anything. It never entered her head that the women were suffering torments seeing all those delicious things within arm's reach.

Granny Novotny spoke of her struggle with her conscience. She had been too shy to ask the elegant lady from Berlin for a chocolate. And then at night the light had been switched off. Granny Novotny had been unable to sleep, tormented by her pain, and by her desire for a nibble. For hours she had tossed about, trying to overcome her craving for something sweet. In vain. Her code of behaviour had told her that one did not do such a thing. But a thousand little devils had whispered to her: "She's got so much, she'll never notice." And so Granny Novotny had helped herself.

Lola was swallowing hard as she listened to all this. She got Sister Eva to pass her her handbag, fished out a fifty-mark note, and gave it to her. "Please, Sister, send someone out to buy some liqueur chocolates with this. Granny Novotny shall have her fill of them. And all the others in the room too."

Sister Eva stood there irresolute, looking at me. I explained to Lola that the liqueur chocolates were of West Berlin origin. Nothing of the kind was obtainable in our shops.

Lola stared at me uncomprehendingly. Evidently since marrying Under-Secretary of State Oehmichen she had never been inside an H.O. store—our East German State-owned retail shops. "Well, then, get whatever there is to be had," she said, confused. "Chocolate, or chocolates, or something of the kind." The guilty conscience of the privileged seemed to paralyse her normally all too active tongue. But the few words she had spoken had already betrayed the fact that luxury goods from the much-maligned West were just a matter of course to her. There is nothing that so infuriates the ordinary people in our country—the people for whom the spectacle of a classless society is continually being enacted—as the privileges enjoyed by the ruling caste.

I am certain that Ward 16 did not run out of conversational material that day. I have no doubt that each one of the women there treated Lola to a very thorough lecture on what conditions were really like in the shops which they had to patronize, and on their everyday domestic economy. After all, that is the favourite topic of our women.

11

SCRUBBING-UP is a special ritual for us surgeons every morning. It takes a quarter of an hour. During that time we are by ourselves in an anteroom of the operating theatre, and are therefore able to talk about subjects which we should have to avoid elsewhere in the hospital or in the street. For this purpose quite definite conventions have crystallized. Even here no one dares to revile the State or the Party openly, since you can never be sure that some Sister, some nurse, or some young doctor is not a police informer. In our discussions we therefore keep to the twilight zone between the permitted and the forbidden. And if somebody should let slip an unguarded remark, then everybody immediately tries to obliterate the meaning of his words. I well remember the agonizing moment when, upon Ulbricht's appointment as a State Counsellor, one of the young housemen breathed a sigh: "Ah, well, we should all have started as brothel-keepers." Dr Kukowa was the first to recover: "Hotel-keepers? My dear young colleague, you must have slept through the social science lecture. State Counsellor Ulbricht never practised the capitalist occupation of hotel-keeper. He is quite an ordinary man, the son of quite ordinary people."

The young houseman nodded his head gratefully. He immediately abandoned the dangerous subject.

I must explain at this point that the social science lectures are compulsory for the students of all university departments, no matter what subject they are taking. These lectures deal at considerable length with the history and ideology of communism.

My operation team that morning consisted of myself, with Dr Kukowa as my first assistant, and young Dr Horst Reinfeld as my second assistant. For ten minutes we soaped our forearms. Then we lifted our hands to let the water drip off our elbows. We then rinsed our hands in dishes containing 70 per cent. alcohol, so that the very last germs should be killed. The Sisters helped us put on our theatre gowns and masks. We were ready to start operating.

The operating theatre had been damaged by bombs during the War. It had since been repaired, but the material used had been of poor quality. The walls were unsightly, because some bad patches had been covered with fresh plaster. There were several cracks in the ceiling.

I took up my position on the right side of the operating table and asked Sister Helga to pass me the sponge-holding forceps with a gauze sponge soaked in methylated ether. This I brushed several times over Frau Steinkopf's abdomen, thus sterilizing it. A second sponge was dipped in iodine. It spread an astringent odour, and stained the operation area brown. I clipped the towels to the skin of the abdomen, so that only a rectangular space was left bare for the operation. I slipped on my golden-yellow rubber gloves. I exchanged glances with Ute Weltz, the assistant doctor sitting at the patient's head, in charge of the anaesthetics, to make sure all was ready for me to start.

With the scalpel I made an incision from the end of the breastbone vertically towards the region of the navel. White and soft, the skin gaped open. The next incision, a little deeper, went right through the fatty tissue. A little more pressure was needed to cut through the fascia, the layer of fibrous tissue lying underneath the skin. Now the stomach was revealed as a limp grey sac. At its lower end it was connected by a fat-like tissue with the horizontal part of the large intestine. I severed this tissue and pulled the stomach forward.

I could feel with my fingertips, from the outside, the patient's ulcer at the so-called lesser curvature near the cardiac end of the stomach. When an ulcer is situated so high up it is unfortunately necessary to remove the major part of the stomach. I decided to perform the operation known to every surgeon by the name of Billroth II. It had been developed by Theodor Billroth, the great nineteenth-century Viennese surgeon. This method involves the separation of the stomach from the duodenum, the removal of the part containing the ulcer, and the provision of a new link between the remainder of the stomach and the small intestine.

"A little more ether, darling," Reinfeld whispered to Ute.

I looked up in surprise. Ute, bending low over her patient, was obviously embarrassed. Since when had those two been on terms of endearment? As Reinfeld also seemed confused I pretended not to have heard anything.

I cut through the duodenum below the pyloric sphincter. Sister Helga passed me the needle-holder with its crescent-shaped needle already threaded with catgut. Catgut is the most important suturing material in surgery, and, as the name implies, used to be made from the guts of cats. Nowadays, however, catgut made from the guts of sheep is commonly used in most countries. The East German Foreign Trade Board, however, purchases for us the cheapest and poorest types of catgut, usually those which find no other purchaser in the world market. We have a lot of trouble with these sutures. They keep breaking.

Just as infuriating are our needle-holders of East German steel: they lack springiness, and make it difficult to guide the needle. Kukowa and Reinfeld were sympathetically watching my efforts to get the needle through the outer layers of the duodenum. I had already successfully performed a suture of the softer mucous membrane, but now, as I was trying to push the needle through the tougher outer layers, it kept twisting in the needle-holder and being deflected sideways.

"Socialism can be victorious only, Herr Oberarzt, if we all put our shoulders to the wheel," Kukowa mocked.

There was in fact nothing else I could do but increase my pressure on the needle. The needle-holder was not sufficiently elastic to keep a hold on it. I had to grip it hard between the clamp-jaws. Suddenly there was a faint metallic click. The tip of the needle had snapped. I saw it disappear between stomach and liver. That really was the last straw!

I do not have to explain the difficulty of finding a piece of thin metal an eighth of an inch long, and by now covered with blood, in the abdominal cavity. Twenty minutes passed before we had finally fished out the needle. Our time, of course, did not matter. But the longer a patient remains opened up, the longer he has to be under the anaesthetic, and the greater also is the risk of infection.

We did not suspect at that stage in the proceedings that the risk of bacterial infection would in fact prove the least of our troubles. After a great deal of effort I succeeded in completing the suture of the outer layers of the duodenum with another needle-holder. The duodenum was now closed at its upper end.

And now began the second stage of the operation. I resected the greater part of the stomach, including the ulcer. There was only a small part of the stomach left, which I had now to link up with a loop in the small intestine. The stomach is not as important for digestion as is usually assumed. Strictly speaking, it acts only as a storage space for the ingested food. True, its acids and enzymes ensure a certain amount of preliminary digestion, but if necessary the intestines can do the entire job by themselves.

I sewed up the remainder of the stomach to form a greatly reduced sac, and placed a loop of the small intestine into the suture. I slit open the side of this loop, so that the contents of the stomach could pass into the intestine through this new opening. The slit was so arranged that a communication was maintained with the bypassed part of the small intestine and the duodenum. The reason for this is that the secretions of the gall bladder and the pancreas run into the duodenum. In our patient these would now flow past the stomach and mingle with the food at the new stomach exit we had made.

I had just completed the last suture at the new connexion between stomach and intestine when the silence in the theatre was shattered by the crash of an explosion. The windows rattled. A moment later we were all enveloped in a grey cloud of dust. Instinctively I grabbed one of the towels and pulled it over the patient's exposed abdomen. We none of us knew what had happened. We were in the middle of a cloud of chalky dust which made breathing difficult, and made our eyes smart. As though through a fog, I saw Kukowa's furious face. We all looked as if we had come in from a blizzard. Everything in the theatre was covered with a thick layer of chalky grey dust.

Carefully I lifted the cloth from the patient's abdomen. I had reacted quickly, but not quickly enough to prevent crumbs of plaster from falling into the exposed abdominal cavity. Later we learnt that the ruined walls of a church near the hospital had been blasted. The shock wave had brought down the cracked plaster ceiling of the theatre. Aghast, we stared at the layer of chalk in the open wound. Unless a miracle happened this white covering must become Frau Steinkopf's shroud. But a surgeon cannot rely on miracles.

For the next half-hour we tried desperately to fish out all the crumbs and specks of chalk with forceps or with our fingers. We were cursing like galley-slaves. Kukowa was the first to realize that angry language could not undo the damage. He reverted to his form of cynical humour: "That's what you get for compromising with the bourgeoisie. It was the bourgeois who built this hospital. And our Party has always warned us that the edifice of the bourgeoisie is crumbling."

Dr Kukowa never expected anyone to smile at his remarks. Indeed, it was wiser to listen to them with a dead-pan face. For once we did not have to try hard to remain serious. I kept seeing Frau Steinkopf's laughing face before me—this robust, cheerful, and optimistic woman who had so confidently looked forward to her operation. She had proudly told me about her three children. Only a few days before, during visiting time, I had met her husband, a big, hulking master locksmith. It was obvious that theirs was a happy marriage, forged by difficult times.

I ordered a solution of penicillin, streptomycin, and Euvernil, a sulphonamide drug, and poured 100 cc. of this anti-bacterial mixture into the opened abdomen. We moreover injected tetanus serum and fitted a rubber drain so that the pus which was almost certain to form could drain away.

The operation had taken the best part of four hours. And we could not help feeling that most probably it had all been in vain.

12

Although I was kept pretty fully occupied by my work at the hospital, I was also the factory doctor at a State-owned textile mill called 'Fortschritt,' meaning 'Progress.' Because of the chronic shortage of qualified medical personnel, most of us doctors in East Germany have to hold down two jobs. Only in this way do we achieve the high incomes for which we are often envied by hospital doctors in West Germany. But this superficial impression is very deceptive. Our doctors are paid in accordance with a collective agreement. Under the agreed rates I, as an *Oberarzt*, was entitled to a maximum salary of 1550 DM monthly, with the prospect of an old-age pension amounting to 60 per cent. of this salary. Comparison with doctors' salaries in West Germany, however, is impossible because the cost of everything beyond the most basic everyday requirements is incomparably higher. True, potatoes and bread cost less than in the Federal Republic, but nearly all other foodstuffs, textiles, and ordinary consumer goods cost twice or three times as much. A motor-car which in the West is owned by a great many people earning considerably less than 1500 DM is hardly within the reach of an *Oberarzt* in East Germany, unless he takes on a second job.

On the afternoon following the operation on our unfortunate Frau Steinkopf I drove my little Wartburg car out to the Progress factory on the outskirts of the town. The dilapidated workshops, where two thousand people were employed, did not live up to the undertaking's proud name. My first-aid post was accommodated in a hut which was pervaded with the sickly smell of rotting wood. While I was at the hospital the post was manned by an elderly woman who called herself Sister Suzanne, but who had never taken any nursing examination and knew very little of the requirements of her job. One thing she had learned in the course of her activity was how to pretend to be sick herself. A great many workers complained to me about her laziness and incompetence.

The moment I drew up outside my hut the loudspeakers throughout the factory blocks came noisily to life: "The factory doctor has just arrived. Surgery starts at once."

There were surprisingly few patients that afternoon. As a rule January is the peak month for influenza, and means a lot of work. As the factory doctor I could confine myself to the treatment of slight troubles, rheumatic pains, stomach-aches, and colds. Any doubtful cases I sent to the polyclinic, or to one of the hospitals for examination.

One of my first patients that afternoon was a woman who worked in the spinning-shop. Three weeks previously she had slipped and fallen against a machine. As she had a three-inch cut on her leg, I had ordered her to be driven in one of the factory cars to the Casualty department of our hospital. The wound had healed well, but the patient told me that she would never again set foot inside our hospital. Having her wound stitched up, she said, had been terribly painful. I was rather surprised to hear this, as I knew the woman was not particularly given to being sorry for herself. To my amazement she then told me that the doctor had stitched it up with practically no local anaesthetic.

"Do you know the name of the doctor who treated you?" I asked.

"Dr Hansen."

Every time it was Hansen. The way he treated his patients was quite inexcusable. To have him on the hospital staff was a burden, not only from a medical point of view, but also from a moral and human one. But what was the use of getting worked up about it? Let the radio blare, but don't let it penetrate into your private world. . . . I was beginning to notice how difficult it was to live up to this philosophy.

Two hours later the waiting-room was empty. It occurred to me that I might take the opportunity to gain a new ally in my flat-hunting campaign. Still wearing my white gown, I walked over to the administrative block and knocked at the door of the works manager. He was a National Prize winner, the holder of the highest distinction to be earned in our elaborate system of orders and honours. The works manager scratched his grey head when he had listened to my request. He used to be an ordinary spinning worker, a hard-working and efficient man. In 1953 or thereabouts he had been in the news repeatedly for greatly exceeding his norm. He had been publicized as an example, he had been awarded the National Prize, and he had finally been appointed works manager. No doubt he was an influential man. But I was probably expecting too much even of him if I thought that he could get me a flat. He too could give me only a noncommittal promise that he would do everything in his power to help me. I had now collected a sufficient number of promises.

13

PAUL KRANICH pounced on me near his 'peace corner.' He had just replaced the complaints book on the red-covered table, having taken the precaution of hiding it away before the visit of the Central Committee delegation.

"Dear colleague doctor," he cooed, "I believe you are looking for a flat. Well, then, you see, in that case you will have to do something for progress and for the community. We intend to set up in our hospital the first socialist brigade."

"I've read about it in the paper," I replied coldly.

"Quite so, quite so. It is a great programme for peace. Dr Hansen's section was going to form a socialist brigade, but Comrade Hansen unfortunately has had to back out because of his many obligations as a trade-union official. It is up to you now, dear colleague doctor, to come to our aid by setting up a socialist brigade in your department."

I had much difficulty in dissuading him from this plan. Socialist brigades consist of a doctor, the nurses, the Sisters, and the cleaning staff of a ward. The Party wants each ward, wherever possible, to represent a socialist brigade. In our hospital not one had so far been formed. The duties of these brigades are a curious mixture of nonsense and obvious platitudes. The members undertake to be clean, punctual, and reliable, to read their professional papers, and to pass on new information. They take on a number of obligations, like being economical in the use of bandaging material, medicines, and electric power; they conclude sponsorship agreements with socialist brigades in other enterprises, and take part in the kind of competition where everybody wins.

Paul Kranich realized that I was not to be talked into this tomfoolery. But he did not let me escape either: "We want to become a socialist hospital. And that involves preventive medicine and accident prevention. You must lecture to our staff on preventive medicine and accident prevention."

Since the lecture was to be a month ahead, I agreed to give it, if only to get rid of him.

Before starting my afternoon turn in Casualty I had a quick look at the two rooms which were being kept free for the foreign Head of State. Frau Gummer, grumpy as always, told me that a commission from the Party's District Committee had been round in the morning to convince themselves of the suitable condition of the rooms. One had to be careful what one said to Frau Gummer; she belonged to the trade-union committee, and spent much time on work for the Party. Ever since her husband had left her three years ago and gone to West Germany she had been bristling with hatred for the Federal Republic. It is quite usual in our country to praise a West German cigarette or a new model of a Western motor-car, and nobody regards such approval as a 'political' remark. But in Frau Gummer's presence it was wiser to avoid such observations. This was generally known among the hospital staff and the regular patients. With any new arrivals on the staff she would have spirited arguments. Her first name was Rosa. We used to call her our Red, Red Rose. Kukowa, in his mock-pompous style, had described her as 'our rose-coloured shield against Western provocation.'

Rosa would bully our male nurse Nitschke whenever she could. Nitschke had once owned a chemist's shop and, like many other former chemists, become a male nurse when his shop was nationalized. Although a quiet man, Nitschke did not always succeed in swallowing his annoyance. To-day he had made a few derogatory remarks about the State visit, and thereby aroused Rosa Gummer's anger.

Some of the patients arrived late for their treatment because they had been forced to make big detours. The principal streets in the town had been cordoned off by strong units of police, and it was impossible to get within two hundred yards of the hotel where the visitor was staying. The grey façades of the houses were hidden behind fluttering flags and colourful slogans. These assured the visitor that the entire population of the town welcomed him. Outside a cinema was the inscription: 'We all clasp your hand and congratulate you on the successful building of socialism in your own country.'

With these cheers in writing the foreign Head of State had to content himself—for on his drive through the streets to receptions at the Town Hall and at the Party District Executive he saw nothing of the town's population beyond a thick line of People's Policemen. Escorted by Zis and Sachsenring cars, the visitor rode in a black limousine—oddly enough a West German Mercedes 220 S—through almost deserted thoroughfares. All this I learned from the patients in Casualty who had to come from the other side of the town. According to the rota, I was to be relieved at the end of my shift by Hansen, who was down for night duty. But instead of him Dr Wolfgang Busch appeared, a good friend of mine. He was only two years younger than I, but because of prolonged captivity in Russia had lost much time, and was only now preparing for his specialist's examination. We were on Christian-name terms, and frequently visited each other in the evenings. Our wives also got on well together.

I was surprised to find him taking on an extra turn of duty at a time when he needed every minute for revising for his examination.

Busch, a little shorter than myself, plump, and with dark hair, lit a cigarette and leaned against the glassed-in notice-board which displayed the Ten Commandments of Socialist Morality. "Politics, old boy," he said slyly. "I need Hansen's help to pass my exam. And that's worth an occasional night shift."

I regarded him in disbelief. Surely Hansen's influence could not extend that far? Knowledge and skill, rather than good relations with the Party, were what mattered in a specialist's examination. Admittedly the chairman of the examination board was Dr Tschauner, the Regional Medical Officer, but all the questions were asked by professors of surgery, medicine, and gynaecology. Surely these professors must regard a trade-union committee chairman as a mere nobody?

But Wolfgang Busch saw things differently. His worst enemy in the town was Dr Schwiers, the District Medical Officer. They both came from the same provincial town, and had had a serious quarrel there. In 1955 the District Medical Officer had to attend some important meeting in Berlin, and had chosen Dr Wolfgang Busch, then a young houseman, to accompany him. But Busch made all kinds of excuses. In the end, when Schwiers tried to put pressure on him, Busch sent him his refusal by registered post. He thought then that he could afford this bold course of action since he had just been promised a junior post at our hospital. He was not to know that a year later the District Medical Officer would be transferred to our town.

Dr Schwiers admittedly was not concerned with the specialist's examination, but he was the immediate subordinate of the Regional Medical Officer who was chairman of the examination board. Busch and I simply did not know whether it was within the power of the District Medical Officer to prevent anybody's admission to the specialist's examination. But Hansen had hinted at that possibility, and promised Busch, in exchange for an occasional favour, to restrain the District Medical Officer (whose regular table at the Ratskeller he sometimes shared) from damaging Busch's career. Of course, it was shameless blackmail, but what was Busch to do if he did not wish to jeopardize his future?

14

As I climbed the last few steps of the well-worn stairs leading up to our small attic room I was met by the aroma of roast meat. On the table, which was covered with a white tablecloth, stood a bottle of Crimean champagne. Ruth greeted me in the red silk cocktail dress which she had worn at the last physicians' ball. It went well with her dark hair and her expressive features. Rouge and powder covered her usually tired face, and made her look as young as she in fact was.

I frantically searched my memory to discover the occasion for this celebration. A wedding anniversary? A birthday? Or could there have been any news from the District Medical Officer about the flat promised us?

She saw my perplexity, and no doubt had not expected anything else. I never had a head for dates.

"But, Peterkin," she said, with the special indulgence loving wives have occasionally for their husbands' weaknesses. She had a whole list of special names for me, and chose from it according to her mood and the occasion in hand. Peterkin was the most loving of them. If she wanted to annoy me she called me Kazimir; when appealing to my masculinity she would call me Jackie; when she was angry she would call me Emil; and in moments of extreme happiness Waldemar.

"Peterkin," she said, "six years ago to-day we met one another." I kissed her to make up for my forgetfulness. It was too late now to get any flowers, but she had anticipated me by buying a bunch of tulips herself.

We sat down to our little feast, and in between mouthfuls treated ourselves to the colourful tatters of our most beautiful memories. Six years ago . . . It had been a frosty winter day, with snow and ice on the roads. A lot of accident cases were brought into Casualty. One of them was a young girl student of philosophy, about to leave for Leipzig for the beginning of the new term; she had slipped in the square outside the station and broken her leg. A pale girl with an expressive face and dark, wavy hair. As I was setting and plastering her leg I was pleased, probably for the first and only time in my life, that our poor-quality East German plaster took such a long time to set. During the following days I spent more time by the bed of the girl student than with any other patient. That was how it started. Two years later we were married.

We clinked our glasses of sweet champagne. We drank to the past. And also to the future. To our next year, our seventh year. Ruth asked how I saw the future. I suspected that she was again about to persuade me to forsake everything and to go over to the West. I was always surprised at her insistence, since most wives in our country advise their husbands against the leap into the unknown. Most women have a horror of sudden change. They are reluctant to give up what they have painfully acquired, and cannot face the idea of a fresh start from scratch.

Perhaps Ruth was different merely because we were still living in our attic. Once we had moved into a decent flat she would probably see things differently.

She was regarding me searchingly. "Tell me, Jackie, in the long run, how will you be able to bear it? I mean the compulsion, the intolerance, the conflicts with your conscience as a doctor?"

"Do you think my conscience would be easier if I left my patients here in the lurch?" I returned. "As a doctor I am needed here far more urgently than in any other—possibly more beautiful —spot."

"But you are wearing yourself out as a human being," she said anxiously. "You are not the type the Party likes. There's no future for you in this country. What use are all your ideals if you become a nervous and moral wreck? As a wreck you won't be much use to your patients either."

I lit a cigarette to gain time for my answer. "Ruth, I'll try to explain to you how I think about it," I said carefully. "In our hospital we've got a radio which we can't switch off. It's on all the time, and it is a nuisance. But we can train ourselves not to hear it any longer. Others may rule that the radio must remain on. But they cannot compel us to listen to it."

"It doesn't strike me as a very compelling philosophy for a doctor," Ruth replied acidly. "Where d'you get it from?"

"From the wife of Under-Secretary of State Oehmichen, who finds herself in the same situation in her private life." I tried to change the subject, because I did not wish the evening to end on a note of bitterness. But Ruth persistently returned to her subject. I could feel that she was jealous of Lola, although she tried not to show it. "And what about Angelica's schooling later on?" she persisted. "What about her having to undergo this Communist education; what about her being alienated from our influence? How does all this match up to your theory of the radio?"

All I could hear in her words was the hidden reminder that I had obligations not only towards her but also towards our daughter. Yet Angelica was only fourteen months old.

I got up from the table, offended. "You know as well as I do," I said angrily, "that the school problem won't become topical for the next five years. But that's just like you: if you can't convince me you resort to some emotional argument. I'm tired of arguing with you about the most important questions in our life. Good night."

I went to bed without another glance at her.

15

THE following morning I drove to hospital without breakfast. Ruth was sulking. Women don't like admitting that they have been wrong, I kept telling myself. The question of our daughter's schooling was surely not a pressing problem. But what about five years from now? And what would I have said if Angelica had been five years older? I could not answer this one. Perhaps I was still too tired. At any rate, I was glad Ruth had not put this question.

As we were scrubbing-up I asked Kukowa casually: "What does one give one's wife if one wants to divert her from unnecessary worries?"

"The women in our country are happy and have no worries," Kukowa answered solemnly. When he noticed that my question was meant seriously he continued in medical jargon: "The prescriptions indicated for the treatment of worry range from a simple bunch of flowers to a fully furnished flat, Herr Oberarzt."

"Well, now," I said with a smile, "suppose you had a case that was serious enough, but not alarming?"

Kukowa thought for a moment. "A television set. Television is a wonderful distraction. To the lonely woman it brings the whole world into her home."

His advice seemed to me of purely academic value. Admittedly, television sets can be seen in all department stores and electrical shops, but the delivery period is about two years. I told him as much.

"Ah, but only with our East German models which are in such colossal demand," Kukowa objected. "If you are prepared to content yourself with a capitalist television set, Herr Oberarzt— say some West German make—you could probably have it in your flat to-morrow."

I pricked up my ears. Kukowa fell silent for a moment as a male nurse came in to collect some cottonwool. When we were alone again he whispered that he knew a young man who could supply West German sets. Admittedly, they cost DM 4500, allowing for the rate of exchange and a small profit for the dealer.

Over the years we had all learned the wisdom of always having a substantial sum of ready cash at hand, since in our country you must be able to make your purchases whenever an article is available.

The next day a young man called on me at the hospital. He was about twenty-two, and did not introduce himself. Within the next two hours or so, he said, a large-sized package would be delivered to my flat. Kukowa had been as good as his word. That night we had a television première in our attic.

16

F<small>RAU STEINKOPF'S</small> condition had deteriorated considerably. At first she had got over her operation quite well, and on the following day looked reasonably fresh. Her optimism seemed to conquer all difficulties. However, on the third day after the operation her face was ashen grey and sunken. She felt limp and exhausted. Her abdomen appeared very taut. Evidently the crumbs of plaster had caused an irritation of the peritoneum. She was vomiting green bile. That was an indication of atonia of the stomach—that is, a paralysis of stomach and intestine. It occurs there when digestive secretions accumulate in considerable quantities. We introduced a tube through her nose into her stomach to relieve her of the tiresome and debilitating sense of wanting to vomit. I prescribed Neoeserin to stimulate her intestines.

Whenever I found time during my various administrative duties I went to look at Frau Steinkopf. Her violent vomiting had led to a loss of salt and water. This in turn affected her circulation, so that her lungs now became affected. A rise in her temperature indicated incipient pneumonia.

Lola, who had to watch all this from the next bed, was depressed. The other patients had also become quiet. Granny Novotny had folded her hands and was praying for the life of the plucky woman. Needless to say, none of the patients knew the cause of the crisis. Although the fall of the ceiling during the operation was the chief topic of conversation among the hospital staff, they all tried not to worry the patients unduly.

I had to spend a great deal of time during those days in supervising the repairs to the theatre on my chief's instructions. For the moment, of course, the theatre was out of action, and we had to get through our list by using the other two theatres. Although we had bricklayers and painters on the house staff, a full ten days passed before the ceiling was finished.

Of all my patients, Frau Steinkopf caused me the most worry.

Her temperature had risen to 104. She was breathing in short gasps. Her heart was pounding. She was tossing about on her bed delirious. A grave attack of pneumonia was threatening her life.

Not until three days later, after we had injected a lot of penicillin and streptomycin into her, did she calm down. She could breathe deeply again, and take small quantities of food. Her temperature went up only in the evening. We were beginning to hope that she had got over the crisis.

If there had been a spare bed in any of the other wards I would have had Frau Steinkopf transferred. The atmosphere in her ward was noisy and restless, for Lola was still having a lot of visitors. Frequently people from some Ministry or the Party would come and see her, or artists giving performances in our town, or friends passing through on their way to winter sports. I saw delegates of the Party's Regional Committee and of the local committee of the National Front, and on one occasion I caught sight of the District Medical Officer, but he clearly avoided me for fear I might worry him again with my requests for a flat.

One of the visitors who called repeatedly must have been Lola's husband. Only by chance did I learn from the young woman in Reception that Under-Secretary of State Oehmichen had called several times on visits to his wife. Lola had never mentioned her husband's visits to me. In fact, she hardly ever spoke about her husband, although we had long chats on many occasions.

The ups and downs of Frau Steinkopf's condition made it necessary for me to look in at Ward 16 more often than at any other ward, and to stop there for longer periods of time. Eventually, after an anxious fortnight, I was able to assure the master locksmith that his wife was now definitely out of danger.

17

Eʀɴsᴛ ᴘғᴇɪғᴇʀ, the blond giant from the outdoor staff, had meanwhile exchanged his blue overalls for the white coat of a male nurse. He had been employed on Ward 4 under Dr Reinfeld as a nursing auxiliary. For the time being he was less of a help than a hindrance, because he was unaccustomed to the work and found it difficult. Now and again he would try specially hard, mainly in order to make a good impression, but his energy invariably evaporated after a few hours.

One afternoon he stopped me in the corridor. "About that socialist brigade, Herr Oberarzt. We want to set up a socialist brigade in our ward to-morrow."

I was surprised. "A socialist brigade? Dr Reinfeld has said nothing to me," I remarked.

"No. Herr Dr Reinfeld is not taking part in it. But we've got to do something. We must do something for the community. Sister Anneliese, Sister Karin, and I, we are all of the same mind. And Frau Piesewitz, the ward maid, is also joining us."

I did not have to ask Pfeifer whether he had already informed the Political Director. The phrase 'we must do something for the community' could have been prompted only by Kranich himself. So at last Kranich had found a team to save him from looking foolish. The fact that not a single doctor was participating was probably only a minor blemish in an otherwise splendid scheme. But Paul Kranich would have looked ridiculous in the eyes of every Party official if the first socialist brigade in the hospital, so pompously announced by him in the local paper, had not in the end materialized.

Besides, Ernst Pfeifer was in no position to refuse any request by his sponsor Kranich. His new post as nursing auxiliary yielded him DM 50 a month more than his work on the outdoor staff, while a white coat carried more prestige than a blue boiler-suit.

And finally, there was that other reason of which I was again reminded by the fact that Hansen had joined us.

Dr Hansen had lately been putting in a more frequent appearance at the hospital in the evenings, even though more often than not he would be gone again half an hour later. No doubt he wanted to refute the allegation that he was never seen in the hospital after 11 a.m. "Lot of work to-day, Herr Oberarzt," he said by way of greeting.

I was about to go, but he caught me by the sleeve. Evidently he wanted me as a witness to his conversation with Ernst Pfeifer. "Listen to me, Pfeifer," he said, in the cold voice of a superior. "Sister Eva has been to see me, and has told me something rather unpleasant. She is having a baby by you. I don't care for that kind of thing among trade-union members. It makes a bad impression in the hospital. I trust that you have decided to marry Sister Eva Schirmer. And the sooner the better—so that the child has a real father when it is born." Pfeifer looked crushed. No doubt Eva had let him in on her worry already. But neither he nor Hansen could know that she had told me all about it first. Otherwise Hansen would not have kept me there as a witness. He had staged it all very well. I could have spat into his cynical face. Strictly speaking, I ought to have shouted at him that he was just as likely to be the father. But I very much doubted whether Sister Eva would still stand by the admission which she had made in a moment of weakness. Probably Hansen had persuaded her to name Pfeifer as the father. After all, that was the best solution for Eva herself.

Pfeifer was not exactly forthcoming in answering. At last he said dejectedly that he did not intend to shirk his duties. But he was in no position to get married in a hurry. Where was the money to come from? He had not saved a penny so far, and the DM 380 a month which he would be earning as a nursing auxiliary was hardly enough to set up a household. It was not even enough to cover the costs of a wedding.

Hansen pretended to be thinking hard. "I've got an idea," he suddenly exclaimed. "We'll arrange a socialist wedding. The first socialist wedding in our hospital. The entire staff are going to take part. It won't cost you or Sister Eva a single penny. Moreover, a couple who have had a socialist wedding will no doubt find a flat soon. And if there is anything else you might need, Pfeifer, you can count on me at any time."

I had to leave them. Pfeifer was still looking dejected, but I felt sure that Hansen would do everything to win him over to his project. I had no idea whether the hospital grapevine was passing the news of Hansen's adventure with Sister Eva. It seemed likely that somebody must have seen them together. For all I knew, rumours might long have been circulating among the nurses. But these rumours would be scotched at once, and would soon be forgotten if Hansen succeeded in persuading Pfeifer into a speedy marriage with Sister Eva. He had planned it all very neatly, that delightful colleague of mine. . . .

18

LOLA'S wounds had healed well. She was now allowed up for a couple of hours every afternoon. I was aware that she was reluctant to return to Berlin, but from a medical point of view I could not justify delaying her discharge. Every day we had difficulties about admitting new patients simply because we were short of beds. Frequently we were forced to discharge patients whom we should have preferred to keep under observation for a few more days.

The Ministry, too, was beginning to press for Lola's discharge. That was why, early in February, I agreed over the telephone to Lola's being collected the following day. The voice at the other end informed me that a car would be calling at the hospital in the late afternoon of the next day. Lola listened with a stony face when I informed her of the arrangements during my afternoon round. She did not say a word to me while I was examining the other five patients. Normally nothing would stop her from talking, even if I happened to be listening to Frau Steinkopf's lungs or examining the reflexes of the other patients.

After my round, as I was sitting in my office filling in forms—a job I always did at that hour—there was a knock at the door. Lola came in, her left arm in a sling, her right hand holding a book and a packet of West German cigarettes. She sat down in the opposite chair and laughed at me without any sign of embarrassment. "I was not prepared for such a speedy discharge, Doctor," she said. "I've got to talk to you before these ruffians take me back to Berlin. How about to-night?"

Her green eyes were twinkling. I could feel my heart pounding. Until then everything had been just a feather-light flirtation. I did not think that she herself was prepared to go any farther. She was the kind of woman to whom it is difficult to say no. But surely this was all madness? She could not possibly leave the hospital. I was still responsible for her as a doctor. I tried to explain to her.

"You are always so earnest, Doctor, so ponderous," she said gaily. "Always carrying such a load of responsibility—it will give you a rupture one of these days! But to-morrow I'm being discharged, and after that I can do as I choose. Have you any time for me to-morrow night?"

"To-morrow your car is coming."

"So what? I can send it away." I was no match for this untamed wildcat. All I could do was hide behind my mask of authority. In the end we arranged to have lunch together in the Ratskeller next day, when she had had her discharge papers.

"Very well," she said. "But when you're in Berlin, Doctor, you've got to visit me. You keep this book carefully. You've probably got no more time for reading than I have. But I've written a dedication on the fly-leaf—and my address."

I saw her again on my round the following morning. But when I came out of the operating theatre at lunch-time I was told that Frau Oehmichen had been collected. The car had arrived earlier than arranged. Granny Novotny handed me a note from Lola. It contained nothing except her telephone number and the brief remark: 'You can always reach me at this number. Yours, L.R.'

Part Two

1

The February sunshine was dappling the hospital block with the first cheerful touches of colour. But to me the hospital seemed greyer than ever after Lola's departure. The place once more belonged to us colourless people. Ruth was spending her evenings in front of the television screen. Busch had withdrawn almost completely behind his books, studying for his examination. Sister Eva walked about with a disgruntled face: her frail body was making very heavy weather of her pregnancy. Frau Gummer nagged and bellyached as always. Granny Novotny was her usual patient self, and Frau Steinkopf was still occasionally troubled by slight relapses.

The only upheaval was in the medical department. There the patients were being cleared out of one of the wards. A thing that would have seemed impossible in view of our chronic shortage of beds was being done upon Professor Brunke's strict orders. Brunke had come to realize that his voluntary reconstruction shifts were hardly likely to earn him the title of Meritorious People's Doctor. He had therefore conceived another idea. A nationalized tools firm had subscribed DM 30,000 for an extension to the hospital. Strictly speaking, half that amount should have been allotted to the surgical department, but Professor Brunke saw a better use for the money. He had a ward cleared and equipped as a 'sleep-treatment ward.' In it he intended to apply the teachings of the great Russian physiologist Ivan Petrovich Pavlov. Pavlov lived from 1849 to 1936, and his theories have been very fashionable in our country for the past fifteen years. To introduce Pavlov's teachings into hospital practice was considered progressive. It was Pavlov who expounded the theory of conditioned responses : that is, that our bodies can be trained to respond to artificial stimuli just as to natural ones. In experiments with dogs and other animals Pavlov discovered that a previously neutral stimulus will, when it becomes associated with food in the animal's mind, cause a salivary response.

Pavlov also taught that prolonged sleep fortifies the body's defences when it has been weakened by sickness. Pavlov enjoys a considerable standing as a scientist throughout the world, but in Russia and her satellites he is revered as a kind of Communist saint. Professor Brunke's decision to set up a Pavlov ward had therefore to be judged a politically commendable action.

One afternoon I ran into Frau Piesewitz, the scrubber and cleaner on the socialist brigade. She was just locking her mop and pail away in the broom cupboard. "Target reached already?" I asked in passing.

She placed her massive arms on her hips. "No, Herr Oberarzt. Got to go to a lecture now. The Director is speaking about that what's-his-name, that Russian fellow."

I stopped in surprise. "What Russian fellow?"

"You know—that sleep doctor. It's part of our educational course."

I thought there must be a misunderstanding. Surely Frau Piesewitz was not expected to sit through a scientific lecture? Two minutes later I climbed the stairs to the nurses' common-room under the roof of the ward wing. That was where the educational courses were held. And there they all were: the men of the outdoor staff, the boiler-men, the laundry women, the kitchen maids, and also a sprinkling of nurses and Sisters. They were waiting for the beginning of the lecture which was advertised on a sheet of white paper pinned to the door: 'Professor Dr Brunke, the Hospital Director, will lecture on the subject: "Pavlov's Teaching and its Importance in the Contemporary Health Service."'

Two hours later I again encountered Frau Piesewitz. She was

back at work. I asked her what the Professor had talked about. "Oh, you know," she said, "about sleep. That sleeping is good for you."

"Anything else?"

"Something about that Russian."

"And what about that Russian?"

"I don't know rightly. But the Director was very angry because so many of us fell asleep."

2

THERE had been frost during the night. On my way from the doctors' car-park to the hospital entrance big puffs of white steam issued from my mouth, almost as if I were a chain smoker. The puffs did not cease when I had stepped through the front door. Filled with forebodings, I touched one of the radiators under the window. Stone cold. Kukowa, who was sitting in his office in his overcoat and with his hat on, but who had left the door ajar, explained. A few days ago water had broken into the opencast workings of the lignite mine which supplied our hospital. Mining operations had had to be temporarily suspended. The small reserves in our fuel store had been used up overnight. New deliveries could not be expected before the evening. We had to prepare ourselves for a day with stiff fingers. This sort of thing happened every winter three or four times.

Kukowa and Hansen accompanied me on a round of the operating theatres. The temperature there was a little higher than out in the corridors. But, strictly speaking, a temperature of 75 degrees was desirable during operations to prevent the patients from becoming cold. Although they cannot feel the cold while under an anaesthetic, their weakened bodies are very susceptible to developing pneumonia. We should have liked to postpone the day's operations until the following day, but because of the long list of outstanding operations to be performed that week it was impossible. We just had to make do.

For us doctors and surgeons the cool theatre was very pleasant. Under an operating gown, cap, mask, and rubber gloves we did not feel the cold. Indeed, with the regulation temperature in the theatre we were usually too hot. But Ute Weltz, who had to sit throughout several hours at the head end of the operating table, looking after the anaesthetics, was performing her tasks with fingers frozen stiff. We could see slight shivers running down her spine from time to time. During a pause between operations she leaned against Dr Reinfeld, who massaged her bare arms, which were red with cold. "That is the warming thing about our socialism," Kukowa mocked, "that it welds cold individuals together into a new unity."

The nurses giggled. Hospital gossip had already reported that Reinfeld and Ute had been seen in the cinema together several times recently—and, a particularly suspicious circumstance, at Russian films. Russian films are seen only by lovers, because the cinemas then are more than half empty.

I had begun to close up the incision. I remarked to Sister Helga, the theatre Sister: "Ever since that operation on Frau Steinkopf I have been waiting for a needle-holder which does not bear the trademark Thuringia. Did you pass on my requisition order?"

Sister Helga shrugged her shoulders. "The only needle-holders available are the Thuringia ones. Stores administration say they can't get anything else."

After the operation Sister Helga came to see me at my office. She had of course understood that I should have preferred to see a West German trademark on the needle-holder. Her cousin, she informed me, was going to Berlin the next morning. He was going to make a few purchases in the Western sector anyway. She could not, of course, expect him to run the risk of smuggling a needle-holder across the frontier; besides, it would be impossible for the hospital to accept such an article without proper invoice. But if I wanted some little things, such as a few surgical needles, he could easily get those for me. I was very grateful to Sister Helga for her suggestion, since the needles of the State-owned firm

Injecta leave a lot to be desired. I should gladly pay DM 20 or so out of my own pocket for needles from West Berlin.

It was much colder in the wards that day than in the operating theatre. The patients had drawn their blankets right up to their chins. Some of them asked for additional blankets. Unfortunately, we could not meet their requests, since we had only a very small number of spares. In Ward 16 Granny Novotny was the only one who was not grumbling. She enjoyed the sense of superiority which her long stay with us gave her over the more recent arrivals. While the others were grumbling about the temperature, she proudly related her experiences last December, when the heating had been out of order for three whole days.

To be perfectly fair, we did not have to wait very long that time. In the early evening the first lorries from the State coal retail organization came rumbling into the courtyard with a load of brown coal which had originally been earmarked for a school. Shortly afterwards our chimney-stack again belched forth the familiar clouds of thick black smoke. They hung in the night sky like flags of contentment and comfort.

Two days later Sister Helga proudly handed over to me the surgical needles and the receipt of a West Berlin shop. I looked at the needles. Engraved on them, in quite minute letters, was the name of the manufacturer: 'State-owned enterprise Injecta.' Sister Helga's cousin had carried coals to Newcastle.

3

OUR weekends were given over to television. I was off duty then, and invariably looked forward to watching the West German programmes on Saturday and Sunday. We had now had our set for three weeks, and it was still a new and stirring experience for us to see the world of our dreams and longings on the small screen in our attic. There, within arm's length, were people who moved so freely, and who spoke so openly and without inhibitions, that at first we were afraid for them. I still remember an interview with an officer who quite casually revealed details about the armament and numerical strength of the *Bundeswehr*[4] in front of the television camera. In another interview an Opposition Deputy argued against shells with atomic warheads being supplied to the West German forces. Or again, I was greatly impressed by a doctor who vigorously criticized the Bonn Government's new plans for a reform of social insurance. When you've been trained from childhood to weigh each word carefully, to keep silence often, or to formulate certain thoughts in cryptic language, then it is quite a shock to realize that somewhere there are people who can say what they think. But we also found to our dismay that we Germans on the two sides of the barbed wire no longer spoke the same language. We feared that, being used to the stifling atmosphere of catch-phrases and promises, we should be unable to bear the crisp and bracing air of a free society. Many of us who had been over in the West on a visit had felt like poor and backward relations, like country bumpkins in the home of prosperous and widely educated cousins. We do, of course, learn a great deal in our country—but the subjects which are talked about and argued about in the West are unknown to us. We also lack the self-assurance and *savoir faire* of our West German brothers.

Television to us is a much more powerful link with the West than is perhaps suspected in Hamburg, Frankfurt, or Munich. What to the West German viewer is mere entertainment is to us a profound experience. And what is more, a dangerous experience, since the West German television programmes are no topic of conversation for the street or the restaurant. Even in a private circle caution is advisable. The previous day's television programmes were the principal subject of conversation during scrubbing-up in the theatre anteroom, but even there we confined ourselves to light entertainment, or at most to sporting events.

If anyone had told me that I should ever become a passionate television viewer I should have laughed at him. But now during the day I found myself looking forward to the evening's viewing.

When I returned home one Monday night I found Ruth in tears.

4 Federal troops.

The corner where our television set had stood was empty. "Two men came and took it away," she said amid sobs. "There's going to be a prosecution," she explained, "because they say we broke the Customs regulations."

Ruth was afraid that I might be arrested. I did not think it would come to that. A clear distinction is made in our country between offences against the economy and offences against the State. Moreover, members of understaffed professions are imprisoned only for very serious offences.

Two days later came a registered letter from the Customs and Import Control Office, informing me that proceedings were being started against me on charges of buying a television receiver illegally imported into the German Democratic Republic. I was to present myself at the office at ten o'clock the following day for questioning.

Punctually at the appointed time I found myself outside the elegant town house built about the middle of the last century. The front door was locked. I rang the bell, and presently a girl appeared wearing the navy-blue tunic of a Customs officer. She wore a green skirt and a dark green tie; on her head was a round, flat cap, like a sailor's, with a black, red, and gold button. The girl asked to see my summons and escorted me up to the first floor. I was told to wait in a bare room containing only a coat-stand and several chairs.

I sat down as far away as possible from the small iron stove, which threw out an intolerable heat. For about half an hour I was left alone with my thoughts and anxieties. Then the door to the next room opened. There, pale and trembling, stood an old friend of mine—Heinz Wolf, the proprietor of a well-known radio shop. We used to play together as children, for my father's surgery was in the same house as the shop which then belonged to Heinz Wolf's father. Wolf was involved in the same affair as I. "Things are looking black," he said. "A very heavy fine, I should think. I doubt if I'll be able to keep the shop."

The officials left us time for a little chat. Wolf told me that the young men who had been smuggling television sets into the country from the West had been arrested a few days ago. They had been made to disclose all addresses to which they had sold their sets.

Now it was my turn. The girl took me to a room where two Customs officers sat behind a desk. Another uniformed official was taking notes. I was asked to sit down. The official in charge of the investigation asked for my personal particulars. He spoke calmly and firmly, but not uncivilly. I had to put on record my financial circumstances. Bank account standing at DM 14,000; valuables, none; real estate, none; motor-car, yes.

These preliminaries over, the officer looked at me hard: "You bought a television receiver which had been illegally smuggled into the German Democratic Republic. Did you know that the set was of West German manufacture when you decided on your purchase?"

"Yes."

"Did you satisfy yourself that the set had been lawfully imported into the German Democratic Republic?"

"I don't know how I could have so satisfied myself."

"Did you demand to see an importation certificate?"

"No."

"You must have known, then, that the set had been imported illegally. Did this aspect not worry you at all?"

I had made up my mind to remain calm, but now I felt an urge for a cigarette. I asked if I might smoke. The officer gave me permission.

He repeated his question. "No," I said. "All I was concerned about was getting a set at last after waiting for so long."

That was all they wanted to know from me. The officer informed me in a matter-of-fact voice that proceedings would have to be started against me for violation of economic regulations. I signed the protocol of my examination and was allowed to go.

Eight days later I was informed of the verdict against me:

(1) The illegally imported television receiver is hereby confiscated.

(2) You are fined DM 450, payable to the clerk of the court.

I owed this lenient verdict merely to the fact that I was a doctor. Heinz Wolf, the radio dealer, whom I met a few days later when visiting my father, had been fined DM 22,000. Evidently they had hoped that this heavy fine would compel him to hand over his business. Fortunately, Wolf was able to raise the money and keep his shop.

4

THE date of my lecture was drawing near. At first I had looked upon the obligation as a nuisance, and had put off preparing my notes as long as possible. When at last I got down to thinking about what I could say on the subject of accident prevention very little occurred to me. There were only two major sources of accidents in the hospital—first, outdated equipment and apparatus that had become dangerous, and second, the plastic-soled slippers of the Sisters and nurses which occasionally caused them to slip on the polished floors. There was not much that I could say on either subject, since these causes of accidents were beyond our control. It was not within the power of my listeners to modernize the outdated equipment, nor could I expect them to buy better footwear. Shoes in our country were simply bad and expensive.

I therefore decided to take time off to make a thorough tour of all parts of the hospital. Although I had been working in the surgical department for the past eight years, there were still many basements, boxrooms, and workshops which I had never been inside.

I started during my lunch-break by visiting the basement workshops of the medical department. In small, dark, dank, and stuffy cellar workrooms I found carpenters, painters, and fitters at their work benches. They were all of them elderly people, some of them old-age pensioners, and they were doing only patchwork repairs. In the room next door was an old tinsmith who was mending refuse bins, instrument trays, and other enamel-ware. There was a smell of dirt and filth in his workshop, because most of the articles were sent down from the wards inadequately cleaned. Accident prevention? The old men stared at me uncomprehendingly. Yes, there had been some leaflet which they had put up on the inside of the cupboard door or in some wall recess. But beyond that they did not want to be bothered with it. They had not had an accident in years, they said.

I also saw much that was new to me in the boiler-houses. The crude brown coal, after being tipped from the lorries, was taken by conveyor belt to a fuel store at a slightly higher level and from there slid down a chute to the boilers. From the accident prevention angle the only point that I jotted down was a narrow catwalk leading alongside the boilers about eighteen inches above the ground. Inattention there might cause a fall and injury. I spent some time in the damp atmosphere of the laundry, among the steam of the ironing rooms, in the musty potato store, and in the kitchen. I ducked along passages and shafts, clambered up iron spiral staircases, looked into the nurses' quarters, and finished up by inspecting Professor Brunke's new sleep-treatment ward.

Needless to say, this last visit was motivated entirely by curiosity. Accident prevention was merely a welcome pretext which now enabled me to look over this ward independently of the official conducted tour planned by Brunke for the following week. Dr Pollak, a thin man with a haggard and crumpled face, who had worked in Russia for two years under an exchange scheme, was my guide. Brunke had entrusted the ward to him because he had studied Pavlov's teachings in their native country, and probably knew a lot more about them than the Director himself. Everywhere there was a smell of fresh paint and floor-polish. On the wall above the door to the ward, between the obligatory portraits of Pieck and Grotewohl, hung a likeness of the bearded Pavlov. There was a red sisal runner in the corridor. Heavy curtains had been hung over the windows, enabling the ward to be darkened even during the day. Notices everywhere called for quiet. There were several tape recorders standing about on which Dr Pollak had recorded sleep-inducing texts.

The whole place looked as if it had been got ready for the Press photographers. So far only three of the beds were occupied by experimental sleepers.

Dr Pollak was intoxicating himself with visions of the future.

"From among these walls a new spirit will go forth," he was prophesying, his bony forefinger pointing at the empty beds. "We shall make a 50 per cent. economy in medicines, and the time spent by patients in the hospital will be reduced by 30 to 40 per cent. You, too, in your surgical department, will notice an appreciable reduction in pressure, as Pavlov's sleep therapy can replace many an operation."

"Why, that's wonderful!" I exclaimed. "And there we were shedding tears over a cholangioscope which was originally to have been purchased with some of the money that your sleep-treatment ward has swallowed up. Perhaps we may now send you our gallstone patients for a good sleep."

He remained serious and matter-of-fact. "Do that. There are many cases on record of gallstone trouble disappearing after sleep treatment. But besides, our sleep ward is going to save such large sums for the hospital budget that the surplus should be enough to buy a great many surgical instruments." It would have been pointless and a waste of time to argue against his optimism. So many people in our country have to live by plans, projects, economies worked out on paper, and statistics showing progress. Yet Dr Pollak was neither a narrow-minded Party man nor an uncritical admirer of everything Russian. He was simply a bit of an eccentric, a man who lived in a world of his own, who was obsessed with Pavlov's teachings. Monomaniacs like that are found among medical men anywhere in the world. But in our country they are potentially dangerous because, provided their beliefs enjoy Party support, they are placed in positions of power.

5

After my tour of the hospital I jotted down a few notes for my lecture. Certainly I did not have to complain about the attendance. Kranich had seen to it that the nurses' common-room was crowded. I do not suppose anybody had really wanted to come, since these instructional classes were invariably held during the lunch-hour. But the excuse of pressure of other work was accepted only in the case of doctors. Consequently, with the exception of Kukowa and Reinfeld, there were no doctors present at my lecture.

I began by enumerating the possible causes of accidents which I had found on my tour of the hospital. A few general remarks about accident prevention I got from a leaflet which Kranich had thrust into my hand just before the lecture. In this way I just about lasted the course.

Kranich was the first to applaud. Then he leapt to his feet and opened the discussion. He wriggled his neck higher out of his grubby collar, and his eyes behind the thick lenses swept over the rows of chairs. As usual, no one had anything to say. Nervously Kranich moistened his lower lip with his tongue. He thrust out his right arm and, palm turned upward, swung it to and fro as though inviting his audience to place charitable gifts on it. Finally he fell back on the well-worn schoolmaster's trick of addressing his listeners individually: "Well, now, colleague Kramer, what do you have to say about it?"

Kramer, a man on the outdoor staff, thought for a moment. Then he summed up his commentary in one word. "Nothing," he grunted.

Kranich did not give up. "And you, colleague Piesewitz?" The mop-and-pail woman of the socialist brigade improved on the last speaker by making a five-word statement: "It's just as he says."

"Target exceeded by 400 per cent.," Kukowa whispered to me.

Kukowa's crack had not escaped Kranich. Like a bird of prey, he pounced on him, and asked him to speak up. "I'm sure we should all like to hear your interesting observation, dear colleague doctor," he crowed.

Kukowa slowly rose to his feet. Clearly he wanted time to prepare a suitable contribution to the discussion. After a rather involved opening he eventually resorted to that grandiloquent style which Paul Kranich was never able to label either genuine or a parody.

"From the lecture we have just heard we must all learn our lesson for our ceaseless task of building socialism. I suggest that we

67

all undertake to reduce the number of accidents at work by 50 per cent. this year. I moreover suggest, as a personal pledge to be taken by all of us, that we should read every day the accident prevention leaflet which our colleague Kranich no doubt will hand out to each of us. I myself will enter my name, together with this pledge, in the book provided in our peace corner, and I hope that all my colleagues will do the same, so that the book will soon be filled to the last page."

For a moment Kranich stood irresolute, biting his lower lip. Unfortunately, he explained, he had only one copy of the accident prevention leaflet, but he would try to get one for everybody. A pledge to read the instructions every day—and, he added, to observe them—was a truly splendid idea. He also accepted at face value Kukowa's jocular suggestion of undertaking to reduce the number of accidents by 50 per cent., though he thought that perhaps one ought not to tie oneself down to a definite figure.

Kukowa's 'personal pledge' was to be a source of much entertainment to him during the next few days, since, in spite of all his efforts, Kranich was unable to obtain any further copies of the accident prevention directives. The leaflet, it was explained, was being reprinted. Before long the subject was forgotten.

Meanwhile, however, the discussion was by no means finished. A Sister from the medical department stood up and demanded that Kranich should supply them with better footwear because her plastic sandals had already caused her to slip several times. Instantly a man from the outdoor staff shot up and reported that his boots were letting in water. He had had several colds as a result.

Things were livening up. One of the women cooks complained about the poor margarine. It spluttered so much that only the other day her arm had again been covered with blisters.

By now Frau Piesewitz had thought of something to say. She had queued in vain for milk at the State retail shop for three days running. "And I haven't seen any decent vegetables for months," one of the laundresses cut in.

It was always the same. Whenever Kranich provoked a discussion all the dammed-up anger about the poor supply situation was vented on him. He tried to pacify the audience with his old clichés—that these were not 'objective difficulties'—but the inter-jections got louder and louder. "Colleagues!" Kranich screamed. "Colleagues, you get these supply difficulties everywhere, through-out the world. Let me just remind you of the disastrous drought last year. And remember that in spite of it you can still buy food at the old low price. But what are things like in the West? In the Federal Republic the price of butter rose so high last autumn, after the drought, that only the capitalists could afford to buy it. For months the ordinary people just stood outside the shop-windows, pressing their noses against the plate-glass. Mothers were crying their eyes out because they could not buy their children any butter. That's what things are like over there!"

The audience had been dished up this fairy-tale so often—ever since the last autumn when long queues formed outside the State-owned retail shops which happened to have some butter—that it had long ceased to have any effect. "Let's stick to the subject, colleague Kranich," a workshop mechanic shouted. "What about the shortage of bicycle tyres?"

Kranich waved his arms. "The supply situation is not the subject of to-day's lecture and discussion. The instructional course is closed."

Muttering darkly, the meeting dispersed. As for the practical result of my lecture on accident prevention, I had an illustration in Casualty two days later. One of our boilermen burst into the room with one hand covered in blood. Through carelessness or absent-mindedness, he had oiled the coal conveyor belt while it was running. Among the many accidents we had had during the past few months this was the most serious. When Paul Kranich heard of the accident he found comfort in the thought that this particular man had dodged the lecture that afternoon.

6

For once we did not have to complain about a shortage of male nurses—a shortage which as a rule is even more acute than that of doctors. Shortly after Ernst Pfeifer had joined us from the outdoor staff, our male theatre nurse Bollmann returned to us. He had left us to become a medical auxiliary with a mobile rural clinic. Medical auxiliaries are a new profession in East Germany, a profession known only in a country with an acute shortage of qualified doctors. A medical auxiliary is a kind of makeshift doctor, without university training. Bollmann had always been anxious to improve himself. During the War he had been a parachutist, as he was fond of telling all and sundry. But as the child of poor parents he had never been able to go to university—otherwise he would have become a doctor. Fate evidently continued to be against him, for he returned to us considerably deflated. He had failed to pass the admission examination for the medical auxiliary class.

Dr Hansen in particular was glad to see Bollmann back, because Bollmann was in charge of the housing sub-committee of our trade-union committee. Hansen therefore did not have to find anyone else to fill the post.

Matron, with commendable foresight, had applied for a new male theatre nurse the moment Bollman put his name down for the examination. However, we did not really expect to get a replacement. To our great astonishment, though, a substitute arrived on the same day that Bollmann returned to us. Since Bollmann resumed his job in the operating theatre, the new man was attached to Casualty for the time being. It was there that Frau Gummer introduced him to me as I arrived for my turn of duty in the morning.

"This is our new colleague——"

"Pütz, from Cologne," the man said, bowing dashingly. "Driven away by the warmongers. I just could not stand working a single day longer for those West German armament kings."

Pütz looked like a waiter in a night-club. Wavy raven hair, sideboards, and a thin line of a moustache above his lip. He had well-manicured hands and good manners.

"Did you work as a male nurse in Cologne?" I asked him.

"Yes, sir, at the university clinic of Professor Lindenburg," he said eagerly. "I worked for two years in a department for seriously ill patients, after I had been deprived of my means of subsistence. I owned a restaurant at one time, but my business was being systematically wrecked. There's no future for honest businessmen over in the West."

Frau Gummer, who scarcely came up to his shoulder, nodded sadly. She seemed much livelier that morning than usual. Without being asked, she went to make us some coffee. All the time she fussed around our handsome new male nurse, casting admiring glances at him. Only after he had addressed her as 'Madame' three times did she coyly point out to him that in our country the proper form of address now was 'Colleague.'

I was not greatly taken with our new colleague. He smelt of stale beer, and was not as well shaved as the rest of his appearance should have demanded. What annoyed me most about him was that he could not even put on a bandage correctly, and generally seemed to possess practically no nursing experience. I was compelled to correct him several times, but he maintained impertinently that of course different methods were in use in Cologne. In the end I left all difficult tasks to Nitschke and used Pütz chiefly for removing old bandages. I did not mind him spending a lot of time at the secretariat with Frau Gummer, or the fact that he would take half an hour to get from Casualty up into the wards. I did not think this strange nurse would stay with us very long.

I was the more surprised when a few days later Matron commended Pütz in the warmest terms. Naturally, she said, he would need a little while to find his feet, but after that he would be one of our most useful men. As a rule she was a fairly good judge of nursing staff. Since none of the doctors wanted to work with Pütz, it was quite natural for Matron to give him more and more special duties. I did not give the matter another thought, especially as there was an instruction to the effect that refugees from the West were to be treated with special consideration.

The extent of the consideration shown to Pütz was revealed to me a few hours later, during night duty. I had been called over to Dr Reinfeld's ward because a young man we had operated on earlier that day had developed a high temperature, suggesting some complication. According to the rota, Pütz was the night-duty male nurse. I asked the Night Sister, a plain girl with freckles, to find Pütz for me.

"Why don't you ask Matron where he is?" she replied acidly. I stumped out angrily, and the girl followed me. "I'm sorry I said that—I don't want to make any trouble," she whimpered. "But he went up to her room at nine o'clock in the evening. I saw him myself. What's more, this isn't the first time. Many of the Sisters can confirm it, Herr Oberarzt. After all, our rooms are on the same floor."

I said nothing and went to my office. Although it was the middle of the night, I furiously rang up Matron and informed her that male nurse Pütz had not turned up for duty.

"Not turned up for night duty?" she repeated in a shaky voice. "Well, now . . . Oh, of course . . . I'm so sorry. I'm not properly awake. Of course, Nurse Pütz asked to be excused night duty. He had some pressing private matter to see to. I think he said he had to help somebody. But he's left me his telephone number. No, I'm afraid you can't ring him—I've got to find the number first. But leave it to me, Herr Oberarzt, I'll see to it that Pütz or some other male nurse turns up as soon as possible."

Twenty minutes later Pütz appeared, seemingly breathless. He wanted to tell me some long rigmarole, but I left him standing and told him I did not need him any longer.

7

I LEFT Kukowa to perform the last two operations on my list, as I had an early afternoon surgery at the Fortschritt works. I stripped off my rubber gloves and climbed up to the second floor of the theatre block. On that floor I had a small office, and there was also the surgeons' common-room. I met Dr Hansen in the corridor. He had likewise finished early because—at least, so he said—he had to go over to the prison where, in his capacity as People's Police Medical Officer, he had to look after some persons detained pending investigation. As a rule we tried to avoid each other, but just then, with lunch-time approaching, we felt like secret allies in our impending battle with Frau Möser, our personal dragon.

Antonia Möser, a short, plump, flabby, and greasy woman of around fifty, was supposed to look after us surgeons. She cleaned out our rooms and served our food in the common-room. But far from being a servant, she really was a tyrant who treated us as she pleased. Whether we got anything to eat, whether our rooms were tidy when we brought a visitor up in the afternoon, whether we should find a clean cup—all that depended entirely on her mood. She regarded herself as the real boss on the doctors' floor, and, as a matter of principle, never knocked at a door before entering. She did not even knock after we had pinned notices on the doors: 'Please knock.' Only when Kukowa added the words 'Frau Möser' in ink, underlined three times, did she knock for three successive days. But during that time she walked about with such a scowl on her face, and left so much dirty crockery standing about, that we were glad to see her return to her old bad habits.

Frau Möser had just laid the table in the surgeons' common-room. She received us in her usual ungracious manner: "What, only two of you? This is getting worse and worse. Expect me to make half a dozen journeys to the kitchen for each of you, eh?"

Her features were an eloquent indictment of the unpredictability and arbitrariness of all doctors as she picked up her tray to bring us our food in covered casseroles. The hospital staff had a choice between a set meal costing DM 1.50, consisting of soup, main course, and dessert, or a simple working man's snack for 65 pfennig. The patients' meals were cooked separately, and were usually better. Hansen and I chose the set meal.

"That was a silly business you got involved in, Herr Oberartz," Hansen said over the soup. "Surely one doesn't have to break the law if one wants a television set?"

I was irritated. I had paid my fine to the clerk of the court the previous day. "Surely it was my own money?" I grunted. "Easy to be wise after the event."

With a superior smile, Hansen put his hand on my arm. "If I may be permitted to diagnose the cause of your trouble," he said, "I would say it was lack of connexions. After all, Herr Oberarzt, who are your friends? Busch, Kukowa, that man Reger who hopped it over the frontier—surely these are no connexions? Why don't you join those who stand for something, the people who could help you when you are in trouble? Why don't you put yourself in my hands? Very well, Herr Oberarzt, you need a television set. Would you like to have one in your flat next week? Don't shut me up—of course, I mean a set acquired in the proper legal way. An Iris 17, for DM 1550, the model you can see in all the shopwindows. Needless to say, without having to wait for the usual two years. I'll tell you what: when you're driving over to the Fortschritt works after lunch, why not stop at the Co-op head office? Ask for Lichtenberg, the man in charge of the consumer goods department, and give him my regards. I mentioned your case to him at the Ratskeller last night. He will be happy to help you at once. And if ever you have some other wish, don't forget your friend Dr Hansen."

I realized, of course, that if Hansen wanted to do me a favour it was not out of love of me. But his offer was so tempting that I promised him to act on his advice. Hansen was obviously pleased. He got down with a will to the boiled beef, which he usually described as too tough. Only the doughnuts, our sweet course, proved too much for us. As we tried to divide them up with the fork they bounced off our plates like rubber balls. Hansen boisterously picked up one of them and flung it against the wall. It bounced back without even leaving a mark. We decided to warn the others who would come to eat after us, and speared our doughnuts to the coat-hooks by the door. It turned out that our colleagues followed our example. For several days afterwards all the coat-hooks of the surgeons' common-room remained adorned with pale doughnuts. Kukowa called them "mute witnesses of our abundance beyond our needs."

My call on the chief of the consumer goods department at the Co-op head office really had the effect predicted by Hansen. Comrade Lichtenberg listened to my request attentively. Then he nodded eagerly and said: "Yes, the chairman of your trade-union committee has already told me that yours is an exceptionally urgent case. I can quite definitely promise you an Iris 17 for next week."

8

WHEN I entered Ward 16 on my afternoon round I found Granny Novotny sitting up in bed with a huge box of liqueur chocolates on her lap. Her shrivelled old face shone like a baked apple. The parcel had been the biggest surprise in her long and monotonous stay in hospital. Lola had remembered her neighbour.

Granny Novotny was so overjoyed that she forgot her pain. The old woman had now been in hospital for a very long time, and few people paid much attention to her. Her neighbours changed frequently. A few days previously we had also discharged Frau Steinkopf, who had successfully survived her peritonitis and pneumonia. That the elegant lady from Berlin should remember her, long after she had returned to her life of luxury, seemed a miracle to the old woman.

It occurred to me that I had found little time to think of Lola during the past few weeks. Well, she had been a pleasant patient, a ray of sunshine in our grey daily routine. We must not either of us attach anything else to our chance meeting. Maybe for a moment we had been in danger of losing ourselves to illusions.

To her the whole thing could have been no more than a substitute for a holiday flirtation. She was used to being admired by men. She needed reassurance. If she had gone on to the winter sports she would have been admired on the slopes during the day and on the dance floor at night. The accident had sentenced her to a forced stay in hospital. What could be more natural than to start a flirtation with the doctor treating her? Holiday flirtations are no more than a pleasant memory after one's return home. They are surrounded by the aura of a fairy-tale landscape, of carefree enjoyment and gaiety. A period in hospital, accompanied by pain, discomfort, and other irritations, is more quickly expunged from the memory.

When I got back to my office Sister Eva handed me a letter. "The same sender's address as on Granny Novotny's parcel," she said with a smirk. I tore open the envelope and sent Eva from the room. The expensive hand-made paper, which had become almost unobtainable in East Germany, was covered in a large, sloping hand. The writing filled the whole page even though the message was quite short.

"Dear Doctor, I've been waiting for your telephone call for three weeks. What's happened? When are you coming to Berlin? Surely you can find some pretext. I've got to talk to you. Yours, L.R." The words 'got to talk to you' were underlined twice.

That was the entire message. But for the sentence about the pretext I might have assumed that she wanted to consult me professionally. As it was, no doubt was possible.

But for the moment there was no time to ponder over the letter. I locked it away in my desk drawer and continued my round. I was feeling uncomfortable, even though I was elated. I meant more to Lola than I had admitted to myself. This knowledge buttressed my ego and flattered my masculine vanity. But that was as far as it would go. I had no intention of finding a pretext for a journey to Berlin. For the time being I did not even worry about replying.

The following afternoon, as soon as I started my surgery in the

76

hut of the Fortschritt works, Sister Suzanne informed me that the works manager wished to see me at once. This could only mean that he had found a flat for me. Full of expectation, I hurried to his office.

"Come in, Herr Doktor; I've got some important news for you," the grey-haired National Prize winner began. "We've got an invitation from the Central Executive of the Free German Trade Union Federation. There's a conference on industrial health next Monday. We've got to send a representative, and you're the obvious man. I shall see to it that you get the day off from the hospital."

"Where is the conference?" I asked hastily.

"In Berlin."

In Berlin. Was I to laugh or to cry? Suddenly the pretext was no longer a pretext. This was an order. You've got to go to Berlin. The works manager's orders. It seemed as if fate itself was instructing me to go. I made what preparations were necessary. As Professor Zöllinger, my immediate boss, had gone to the mountains for a few days, I went to see Professor Brunke, the Hospital Director, the following morning. Even though the National Prize winner was going to get me my special leave, I felt it would only be polite for me to have a word with the Director myself. I came upon him in his anteroom, as he was talking to a People's Police officer.

"Oh, you're just the man we want!" Professor Brunke exclaimed. "Tell me, was a Dr Pütz engaged by the surgical department recently? I don't know any doctor of that name."

"Pütz from Cologne?" I asked.

"Speaks with a Rhineland accent," the officer read from the notebook in his hand. "That'll be him all right."

Professor Brunke frowned. "Was he engaged without my knowledge?" he asked menacingly.

"We've got Pütz on the staff," I confirmed. "But he's a male nurse. There is no doctor of that name."

Professor Brunke whistled through his teeth. "A male nurse? And an old rogue from what I hear. We'll go and have a look at him, Lieutenant."

I told Brunke about my proposed official journey to Berlin and hurriedly took my leave.

Not till evening did I learn from Sister Anneliese—who was a member of the socialist brigade of Reinfeld's ward and invariably well informed about all hospital gossip—what had happened with Pütz. Sister Anneliese, a tall, massive woman with a large wart on her short, stubby nose, drew me into the office, closed the door, and told me excitedly: "As for that man Pütz, Herr Oberarzt, we shan't see him again. He isn't a nurse at all. He's just a common confidence trickster. There was a big dust-up at lunch-time to-day. He was told to pack his belongings and go."

After that Sister Anneliese told me at some length about the final adventure of our splendid refugee from warmongering West Germany. Two days ago, it appeared, he had taken the train after duty to a near-by small town where our municipal theatre was giving a ballet performance. Possibly—though this point was never cleared up—he had known one of the girls of the ballet before. Anyway, after the performance he turned up in the lounge of the small hotel where the girls were resting after the rigours of the performance. The handsome Pütz, being the only male among them, was immediately the centre of their attention. He introduced himself as a doctor from our hospital. Needless to say, he acted the great cavalier and ordered one bottle of Crimean champagne after another. After the first six bottles the waiter discreetly slipped an interim bill into his hand. With a smile, Pütz produced two DM 100 notes from his wallet and told the man to keep the very considerable change. From that moment onward he enjoyed the full confidence of the hotel staff and of his devoted pretty companions.

Most of the girl dancers took the night train home. But the gallant doctor persuaded five of the girls to stay with him. His car, he said, was outside the hotel. He would drive them all back. In the early hours of the morning, when the remainder of the bill was due to be paid, the handsome cavalier's cash was not sufficient. The girls had to lend him a considerable amount. And that was the last they saw of him. A moment later he had vanished. Of his allegedly so luxurious and capacious motor-car there was not a trace.

Hollow-eyed with fatigue and chilled to the bone, the girls had to take the first workmen's train home. A telephone call to the hospital confirmed their suspicion that a Dr Pütz was unknown there. So they informed the police.

Inquiries revealed that Herr Pütz from Cologne had got through several thousand marks at similar drinking parties during the few days that he was on our hospital staff. He had spent his entire re-settlement grant, a sum that is paid by the East German Government to every immigrant from West Germany. Later we learned that Pütz had already served several prison sentences in West Germany, all of them for fraud. He was married with four children. We did not need the police to tell us that he had never been a nurse in a hospital. Our own doctors and nursing staff had discovered that within a few hours of his arrival.

I do not know what became of him. None of us ever saw him again. I have mentioned his short-lived guest performance only because we had more than once experienced much the same thing with West Germans who claimed to have come over to the workers' and peasants' State out of idealism. Our Press and radio keep talking about immigrants from West Germany—people who have chosen communism. I can only say there are a lot of men like Pütz among them.

Matron Margot Kress was suffering from a gastric disturbance for the next few days. She did not show her face in the hospital. But that only increased the amount of gossip about her, and her abruptly terminated affair with the handsome Pütz. What was more, everybody knew now that our attractive Matron had not been the only object of his ardour.

As for the daily work at the hospital, Pütz did not leave much of a gap behind him. We were doubly glad that we had got Boll-mann back. Unfortunately, Bollmann was readier to use his mouth than his hands. Nevertheless, as head of the housing sub-com-mittee he held an important position in the hospital. Since my conversation with Hansen, which had earned me my television set, I had no inhibitions about approaching Bollmann with my housing worries. He put my name down on his list of persons wanting a flat. "Don't you worry, Herr Oberarzt, within three weeks we'll have one for you," he reassured me. "As a married couple with one child you are, of course, entitled to a flat."

With this encouraging thought, I left the hospital on the week-end before my trip to Berlin.

9

I HAD not been in Berlin for years. At one time I used to spend my free days in Berlin on shopping sprees in the Western sector. But the controls had become so strict, and the fines for illegally importing articles so heavy, that these expeditions were no longer worth while.

The headlights of my Wartburg car carved up the darkness. They swept over lonely roads and through sleeping villages. Then came the wide concrete ribbon of the autobahn. I was looking forward to Berlin. I was looking forward to seeing Lola. Why not admit it to myself?

At the crack of dawn I pulled up at the first checkpoint a few miles outside the city. The sentry waved me on immediately he saw the doctor's badge on my windscreen. On the outskirts of the city was another barrier with frontier guards carrying sub-machine-guns. Immediately behind them was a large signpost: 'Berlin—capital of the German Democratic Republic.' Where else in the world, I mused, was there a situation like this? Barriers and heavily armed guards between a country and its capital.

The guard cast only a cursory glance at my blue identity card. The frontier guards had had instructions to treat doctors and other people of importance to the State with particular courtesy. He placed his fingers against the peak of his cap, said: "Hope you have a good journey, Herr Doktor," and raised the barrier.

Along the Stalin Avenue, with its wedding-cake architec-ture, I drove towards the city centre. The building of the Central Executive of the Free German Trade Union Federation was quite close to the sector boundary. As I tried to enter a door-man turned me back: "If you don't mind, colleague, walk round the corner to the other side of the building. This doorway is under enemy observation."

There were about 150 men in the hall—works managers, personnel managers, and factory doctors. Two young men walked up to me and handed me a sheaf of papers.

I was astonished at the plain speaking. There were none of the honeyed phrases and reassuring clichés which were invariably wrapped round the bitter truth at similar events on a lower level—the only kind of meeting I had attended so far. A works manager revealed terrifying figures about incidence of sickness and loss of production in his factory. He did not pull his punches: he vigorously attacked the works doctors sitting in front of him. "Aren't you too easy-going with your certificates, doctors? Aren't you too soft? Aren't you being hoodwinked too easily by malingerers?"

This was certainly the right way to provoke us into frank speaking. A young works doctor, the next speaker, began by telling him some home truths straight away. Quite right, he said; the incidence of sickness was far too high. But the doctors were in no position to reduce it. Certifying people fit for work when they weren't was no answer. Nor could tablets or injections cure a deep-seated reluctance to work.

Someone interjected from the floor: "Surely you doctors ought to be better psychologists? You don't appeal sufficiently to the morale of our workers!"

The young speaker took this one up at once. There were far too many appeals to the people's morale nowadays, he said. For several years now the workers had been subjected to a propaganda barrage. Surely the Party leaders realized by now that words alone could achieve nothing in the long run? The proportion of incorrigible malingerers was by no means as high as some people seemed to think.

There was another interjection: "In that case, colleague doctor, why has there been an objective increase in the number of people absent from work?"

The doctor behind the speaker's desk was in no way rattled. He produced accurate figures about the incidence of the most frequent diseases in his factory. The great bulk of his patients came to him with influenza or colds, rheumatism, circulatory diseases, and various other indications of premature wastage of their strength. These facts forced him to conclude that the people were working under inadequate conditions, frequently in draughty or damp workshops, or in stale air, or at poorly lit work benches. Indeed, working conditions were frequently so bad that the workers were constantly under an entirely intolerable strain, and their strength and resistance were draining away at a terrifying rate. Among women especially, who had to run a household in their spare time, cases of exhaustion were frequent. His demand, therefore, was for measures calculated to conserve the physical strength, and hence the morale, of the working people.

There was thunderous applause from the works doctors. The speaker had sketched the picture which we knew only too well from our surgeries. Much, of course, remained unsaid, because some subjects were taboo. For instance, the stupid irritation of a plan target worked out by someone behind an office desk, the constant strain of a performance norm decreed for every simple operation, and the time wasted as a result of faulty planning or shortage of material. To raise these points would be to touch on the main tenets of the Communist creed. To question these would be high treason.

I realized one thing quite clearly at this meeting: the real disease which we had to fight was communism, or, as our rulers euphemistically called it, socialism. That, of course, was impossible; so we had to confine ourselves to curing a few of its symptoms.

Since any debate of the causes of the waning working morale and the rising sickness figures was bound to remain sterile in the circumstances, the meeting resorted to fine-sounding resolutions. One works doctor proposed that vitamin C tablets should be distributed in all factories to stimulate the workers' resistance to such infections as influenza and colds. This was the kind of proposal dear to the heart of every bureaucrat. Here at last was action! Something was being done! Every worker would personally taste upon his own tongue the State's solicitude for his health. Take these tablets and you won't get sick! And at the end of the campaign there would be statistics showing that the incidence of colds had dropped by so and so many per cent. The proposal was adopted. It was given top priority, since there would be no point in the campaign unless it was started within the next week or two. A senior official announced that the Free German Trade Union Federation would meet the costs of the scheme.

I might add that we had to wait in vain until May for our vitamin tablets. The country simply lacked the manufacturing capacity for producing them in the requisite quantities. Thus the one egg hatched by the conference, amid so much crowing and clucking, turned out to be addled.

10

WHEN the lunch-break came I decided that I had fulfilled my target for participation in the conference. Quite near the trade-union headquarters lived an old uncle of mine, Uncle Theodore. He had formerly been a veterinary surgeon at the city abattoir, and now lived on his pension. He had been a widower for some years. I had intended to pay him a short visit before ringing Lola.

The ancient grey tenement building, on the fourth floor of which Uncle Theodore had his flat, rose like a gaunt castle from the ruins of a large bombed-site. A young woman opened the door. I had already concluded from the names pinned to the landing door that Uncle Theodore shared his large flat with three lodgers.

My uncle was sitting in a comfortable chair by the window, reading a book. He must have been about seventy, but his hair was not yet white, and his broad, flat face showed but few wrinkles. He was delighted to see me, and insisted on my having some of the bean soup which one of his lodgers had made for him. After that we settled down in two chairs by the window, each with a glass of Bulgarian red wine. From there we had a splendid view of the concrete-and-glass skyscrapers in the Western sector.

"You know, I am surprised that you are still here," Uncle Theodore said. "Surely you young people can do so much better for yourselves over there?"

"I am a doctor, Uncle; we are urgently needed here," I replied.

"That's all very well. But if I were your age I would not content myself with looking at the West from here. Or do you belong to the Party?"

"Of course not."

"Listen to me. If at any time you can't bear it any longer, remember that your Uncle Theodore can help you. See that ruin over there, the one that's almost levelled to the ground? That's where the sector boundary runs. The nearest sentries are at the street-corner just here. I know a footpath which can't be seen from where they are. If ever you have any valuables that you want taken across I'll help you." I thanked my uncle, but assured him that I was firmly resolved to stay at the hospital.

Uncle Theodore nodded. He understood. "But in this country of ours something may always happen unexpectedly that makes it impossible for a man to stick to his resolutions. If that should happen, remember me."

I left him towards two o'clock. I drove to the Friedrichstrasse and rang up Lola from one of the State-owned restaurants. When I dialled the number she had given me the grumpy voice of an old man answered. Sorry, said the stranger at the other end, he could not put me through to Under-Secretary of State Oehmichen's flat now. Would I ring again at four?

Two hours with nothing to do! I left my car, took a *Stadtbahn* ticket, and went as far as the Zoo station. During the journey I remembered that an old friend of mine, Dr Ritter, worked at the Westend Hospital. But there was not enough time to go to Charlottenburg, and I decided to ring him up instead. He was disappointed that we could not meet. "Listen," he said, "if ever you've had enough of things over there, you can always count on me. I'm living in the new Hansa district, not very far from the sector boundary. If you want anything stored—my flat's at your disposal. Naturally, also as a springboard for yourself and your family."

I had to smile. So many willing helpers! "Thank you very much," I said. "If the need ever arises . . ."

I replaced the receiver and spent the remaining time strolling slowly through the streets in the Kurfürstendamm neighbourhood. The roar of traffic, the stench of car exhausts, milling crowds, brightly coloured shop signs and neon lights; the staccato of pneumatic drills. An abundance of everything in the shop-windows, the aroma of roasting coffee and frying sausages, hustle and bustle, excitement, the hectic pulse of life. I absorbed it all like some long-missed tonic. At a news-stand I devoured with my eyes the long columns of headlines promising genuine information and reading-matter. I had long stopped reading our newspapers, because they contained nothing but slogans and empty clichés. Elegant women tripped past me on pencil-thin stiletto heels, youths lounged about or else chased trams, the heated, glassed-in terraces of the cafés were packed, well-dressed men with attaché-cases or parcels under their arms hurried importantly along.

I felt as if a long-dammed-up stream of energy had suddenly been released within me. Here I could be myself.

11

BACK in the Friedrichstrasse I again rang the number Lola had given me. Once more I heard the grumpy male voice. Then there were several clicks, and at last Lola was on the line. Her voice, reserved at first, rose to a delighted shriek when she recognized mine. She would come at once, she said. We would meet in an hour's time at the Warsaw café in Stalin Avenue.

I got there a little early, and chose a corner table near the entrance. I surveyed the carpets, the heavy plush curtains, and the old-fashioned upholstered chairs—the hallmarks of proletarian prosperity. The whole place was furnished in the style of a respectable bourgeois restaurant of thirty years ago. The old-fashioned and pompous interior décor matched the over-ornate façades of the Stalinallee, or Stalin Avenue—that showpiece of a street, where all the complexes accumulated by the working-class leaders in their youth *vis-à-vis* a prosperous middle class seemed to have been turned into stone. All the things they had seen in the homes of the hated bourgeois, as tokens of their wealth, they were now copying. They knew no other expression of a higher standard of living.

I smiled at the thought that I was waiting for a representative of that social class—the wife of a Party official who now bore the bourgeois title of an Under-Secretary of State.

The draught curtain in the door parted and Lola stood before me. Radiant and vivacious, she shook hands with me. Under her open camel-hair coat she was wearing an eau-de-nil cocktail dress with a short jacket which covered a neckline that was decidedly daring by East German standards. I felt sure that this was not the usual way for a Party official's wife to dress.

I had plenty of time to admire her, as she did not let me get a word in edgeways. She was positively bubbling over. She had ordered tickets to be reserved for Verdi's *Force of Destiny* at the State Opera, she confided to me. After that we would drive over to West Berlin in her car. She knew a lot of night-clubs there which were great fun.

I pulled her up with a few questions about her state of health. This struck her as an amusing idea, for she sat up like a well-behaved schoolgirl and politely answered all my questions with "Yes, Herr Doktor" and "No, Herr Doktor." She had had no complications of any kind. "Only occasionally, if I do something I shouldn't with my left hand," she said, "I get a momentary reminder. But then I've got my doctor with me to-day, who will surely see to it that I don't do anything I shouldn't, with my left hand or otherwise."

We sipped our coffee complete with the dregs, which are never filtered off in our restaurants because they make the coffee look blacker, and with it munched some cream cake. Lola told me about her plans. In May she intended to take up another engagement as a dancer. Her husband, unfortunately, was against the idea. He was trying to use the after-effects of her motoring accident as a pretext for stopping her from returning to the stage. He was not only jealous like all men in similar positions, Lola explained, but he was also putting the Under-Secretary of State act over rather heavily, and was worried about his reputation.

"When we got married, a year ago, we agreed that I should continue dancing as long as I wanted to," she told me. "He didn't try then to cut short my career."

So she had belonged to the ruling caste for only a year. And what was her background? I did not have to ask many questions. She told me the story of her life without prompting.

Lola Ried came from a good family and had grown up in Munich. Her father had been a well-known painter and a professor at the Academy. Her mother had been an actress, and had subsequently taken up writing. She had been the author of a number of film scenarios. Lola had been taking gymnastic and dancing lessons ever since she was four. At the age of seventeen her first regular contract caused her to leave school. She had repeatedly given guest performances in East Germany, the last time in the autumn of 1958. She had then been in the dumps after an unhappy love affair with a Frankfurt businessman, and in this frame of mind —at least, that was what I gathered from her account—she had met Under-Secretary of State Oehmichen at a reception for artists and theatrical people. Oehmichen, who was about thirty years older than she, was a Party official from Saxony, in East Germany. She had married him, evidently on the rebound from her last disappointment in West Germany. One did not have to be a great psychologist to realize that the marriage of two such totally different partners had not been too happy.

Lola offered me American cigarettes and ordered Russian brandy. "You're so serious, Doctor," she reproved me. "I bet you're not nearly so glad as I am. I really couldn't think of anything nicer than having you here with me. Let's drink to meeting more often."

87

I raised my glass and laughed at her. "I hardly think your husband would approve of that."

At that moment two men in grey lounge suits entered the café. They seemed to absorb Lola's attention instantly. They sat down at a near-by table and lit cigarettes.

"We'll talk about it later," she said to me in a whisper. "I've told you where we'll go after the opera. There we can discuss these things more easily." In a louder voice, she added: "And what are things like at the hospital these days? How is Granny Novotny? And is Frau Steinkopf well again?"

We did not stop long. Lola proposed that we have a snack elsewhere.

"Did you know those two men who sat down near us?" I asked her, as we were walking the short distance to the Hungarian Budapest restaurant at the next street-corner.

"No," she replied calmly. "But I've seen their faces about several times lately."

Not till we got back to her car did I notice that there was a chauffeur sitting in it. She sent him away with instructions to meet us at the State Opera when the performance was over. We then drove to the city centre in my car. "Since my accident my husband won't let me drive myself," she explained. "But we don't have to take the chauffeur with us over to the West. Karl Zielke is a Berliner, a real sweetie, and I can rely on him absolutely. If I slip him a ten-mark note he'll get out at the Friedrichstrasse, before we cross the sector boundary, and have a pint of beer." She settled back in her seat and looked at me from under her eyelashes. "Tell me, Doctor," she whispered, "do you find me attractive?"

I had to keep my eyes on the traffic in the Alexanderplatz and could not turn my head. "Are you fishing for compliments?" I asked drily.

"I adore compliments. Do you remember the first compliment you paid me? You told me you liked the look of my spleen. I'm still proud of that compliment—after all, you're a connoisseur in that field."

I chuckled and put my arm round her shoulder. She leaned forward quickly, and all I held was the camel-hair coat which she had loosely thrown over her shoulders. "Do you want to compromise the wife of an Under-Secretary of State?" she asked, half amused and half angry. "Later to-night, when we are in the West, we'll be simply the girl Lola and the man. . . . I don't think I know your first name?"

"That's a secret which shall be revealed only to the girl Lola, and not to the Under-Secretary's wife," I said firmly.

We drove into the car-park outside the Opera. There was a crush at the cloakrooms and in the foyer. Some people had dressed up for the evening, but there were also quite a few workmen in everyday suits. We had pushed our way through the crowd to the auditorium door when Lola suddenly remembered that she had left the tickets in her coat pocket. I returned to the cloakroom and asked for the coat.

As I turned round I collided with a gentleman in his forties whose face looked familiar. He had receding temples, prominent cheekbones, and a tight, almost lipless mouth. I was sure I had seen him somewhere. Perhaps he was one of the many people at the conference that morning. There was no sign of recognition in his face. So we pushed past each other in silence.

I had seen *The Force of Destiny* in my native town many years before, and still remembered the inexhaustible wealth of moods, colours, and emotions in Verdi's music. The performance at the State Opera, with its lavish splendour of costumes and décor, was an even greater experience. Lola abandoned herself completely to the magic of the music. She seemed to be far away, and totally unaware of my presence. But in the first act, when Alvaro and his secret love Leonora prepare to escape, she studied me curiously from the side. Surreptitiously she caught hold of my right hand. Leonora threw herself into Alvaro's arms and assured him that she was prepared to share with her lover whatever fate had in store. During this scene Lola gently squeezed my hand, and then quickly released it.

From then onward we sat next to each other like strangers, and yet we knew that we were linked by a secret.

During the interval we strolled out towards the entrance and smoked a cigarette in the street. It was a clear and mild spring evening. The cold easterly wind which had been blowing during the day had dropped. As we returned to the foyer we saw a man who had been standing behind a glass door suddenly melt into the crowd. Again his face seemed familiar—full cheeks, a fleshy nose, and a pair of horn-rimmed glasses. This time I knew at once where I had seen him before. He was one of the pair who had taken the table next to ours at the Warsaw café that afternoon. And suddenly I realized who the other stranger was with whom I had collided in the cloakroom before the performance. It was, of course, the other man from the café.

Lola had also seen the plump man with the fleshy nose and the horn-rimmed glasses. We did not mention him, but I could see that she was frightened.

There could be no doubt that she was being watched. It could be that her husband was merely jealous. But it was also conceivable that the State Security Service was shadowing the Under-Secretary's wife without her husband's knowledge. I remembered the case of a high Party official in our town a few years before. The man had been one of the high-ups in the National Front. His attractive wife used to be seen frequently in night-clubs in the company of other men. Twice the husband had been warned by the State Security Service because it was feared that the wife might drift into the company of enemies of the State. For weeks on end she was being watched. When sufficient incriminating evidence had been collected against her the State Security Service struck. The man lost his post and, together with his wife, was transferred to a small provincial town. It was rumoured that the evidence collected against the wife would have been sufficient for a trial. Only consideration for her husband's high position in the Party had caused the authorities to content themselves with shunting them to a safe place in the backwoods.

I did not take in much of the second half of the performance. I kept thinking that Lola was exposing herself to danger whenever she met me. As if she had read my thoughts, she suddenly leaned over to me and whispered: "It may well be that we have to say good-bye to-day sooner than we thought. But I shall come to see you in a few weeks. My first contract will be in your town."

After the performance the bluish-green car which had brought Lola to the Warsaw café was standing near the entrance. But behind the wheel was not Zielke, but another chauffeur. He saluted curtly, and said in a tone which brooked no contradiction: "Unfortunately I must drive you home at once, Frau Oehmichen. You are expected urgently."

Lola cast me a helpless glance. Then she said quite easily: "It was very nice of you, Doctor, to remember your old patient. Give my regards to all our friends at the hospital. I have enjoyed meeting you again. Good-bye."

I was left standing alone among the dispersing opera-goers. In spite of all my anxieties since the incident in the interval, I had pictured our parting differently. In a fury I lit a cigarette. I did not really know whom I was furious with. With the State Security Service because it restricted Lola's freedom? With Under-Secretary of State Oehmichen because he had his wife watched jealously? With Lola, who might well have staged this scene herself because she only wanted to play with me? Or with myself? Undoubtedly I was most furious with myself. For allowing myself to get involved in this adventure.

Full of hurt pride, I got behind the wheel and settled down to a long night drive to my native town.

12

I WAS tired and angry when I turned up in the operating theatre the next morning. Fortunately, I was not alone in my bad temper. The atmosphere in the scrubbing-up room was highly charged, as before a heavy thunderstorm. Busch was rushing around, red in the face, cursing: "Clout them over the head with a hammer—that's what we ought to do. And a damn sight more humane it would be."

I had no idea what had upset him, and was only hoping that his murderous thoughts were not directed against the Party bosses. In which case his words might constitute a 'political remark.' But Busch was talking merely about anaesthetics. He was furious because he had been ready to start operating for the past fifteen minutes, but his patient simply would not go under. The ether supplied by the State-owned Schering works in Adlershof was merely making her sick without sending her to sleep. We had been up against this particular difficulty quite a few times before; the quality of the anaesthetic left a great deal to be desired.

Even Kukowa seemed to have lost his cynical humour that morning. He informed me angrily that he would resign from the Trade Union Federation. Frau Gummer had just told him that unfortunately he could not get the holiday vacancy in the seaside resort of Sellin, on the island of Rügen, that he had applied for. The accommodation available for the summer was simply not enough, so that the local trade-union committee, under Frau Gummer's chairmanship, had been compelled to cross out some of the names. Among these—no one knew why—was Kukowa's. This meant that he and his family would have to give up the idea of a holiday away from home. Hotels by the sea, or in the mountains, where a person might spend his holidays privately, have practically ceased to exist in our country. Private rooms are likewise exceedingly difficult to find because most people letting rooms have their regular summer visitors year after year. Nearly all holiday hotels belong to the Free German Trade Union Federation. A professional person has the choice of applying for his holiday accommodation either through the Trade Union Federation or through the German Cultural League. In short, even our leisure time is so bureaucratically organized that a person who fails to get an official vacancy is virtually condemned to staying at home. "There I go paying twenty-two marks a month contribution to the trade unions," Kukowa grumbled, "and what do I get for it? I'm going to see Hansen after this and hand in my formal resignation."

13

The 'living corpse' was in excellent spirits. His greatest wish had come true. The male nurse Bollmann and his sub-committee had allotted him a flat. Admittedly, it was only two poky little holes which he was to occupy as a lodger in an old-fashioned suburban flat, but for him and his young wife it was their first home.

I had had little opportunity until then to talk to the pale young man. He had been with us only five months, and had always kept himself to himself. His name was Jürgen Warberg, he had qualified in the autumn, and was now doing his first year as a houseman. I had assigned him to Hansen because that was the ward where most work was left undone.

I found Warberg in his ward office during the lunch-break, I propped myself up against the edge of his desk and offered him a cigarette. I had not even known that he was married. He was a countryman, and had a very modest background. I liked him as a keen and willing worker, though he had little personality. He blindly did whatever Hansen instructed him to do, and had even joined the Party because his superior had desired it.

And now I hardly recognized our 'living corpse,' that colourless, pale young man. Overnight he had become vivacious and quite garrulous. "Herr Oberarzt," he said to me, "now life is really beginning for me. Now, for the first time, I have a home. So far I have always lived in digs, and then until recently in a miserable little boxroom in my parents-in-law's house. Everywhere I have felt like a guest, like a kind of refugee—even here in hospital. But now I can feel I bear some responsibility for the first time in my life—even if it is only the responsibility for myself and my wife."

We were joined by Kukowa. He had just had a violent scene with Hansen when he told him his decision to resign from the Trade Union Federation. His announcement had touched Hansen on his most sensitive spot. They had argued for an hour. The argument had ended with Kukowa's remaining a member and declaring himself prepared—though gritting his teeth—to continue paying his high membership contribution. He did not tell anyone what had induced him to change his mind, but I could make a shrewd guess as to what Hansen had told him. A man who leaves his trade union cuts himself off from the community, like a healthy person voluntarily joining the lepers in the desert. His resignation would have been like the mark of Cain in his personal file. He would not have been admitted to the specialists' examination which he intended to sit for next year. His professional career would have been at an end. He would have found it difficult to get another post.

Kukowa had capitulated, but he had also regained his old cynicism. "Needless to say, there is no shortage of holiday accommodation," he began to lecture. "In fact, there is no shortage of anything. The Trade Union Federation merely saw to it that no sand from the Baltic seashore should get into the smoothly running doctoring machine that is myself. I almost believe, Herr Oberarzt, that this comes under your heading of Accident Prevention." At that moment Paul Kranich put his bespectacled head round the door. He was looking for colleague Dr Busch, he explained. Kukowa buttonholed him. "You're just the man we want, colleague Kranich. We are in the middle of an ideological argument. Could you explain to us what the Seifert Plan means?"

Kranich felt as pleased as a schoolboy who is allowed to recite his favourite lesson. He stepped up close to our little group and lectured: "Well, then, the Seifert Plan is the inspired proposal of our colleague Seifert of the railways. It calls for higher performance through purposeful utilization of pauses. This means that all slack periods must be economically exploited. We are just wondering how we could apply the Seifert Plan to our hospital in order to work even more efficiently. Here too we have lulls which are not labour-intensive."

Kukowa was listening attentively. "Colleague Kranich, I've got an idea. I believe that holidays ought to be made labour-intensive. Why should a man loll about idly in the sand?"

Hesitantly Kranich fingered his unshaven chin. He was not sure whether Kukowa was not pulling his leg again. He thought it advisable, however, to instruct the doctor more fully. "There is some misunderstanding, colleague doctor. The Seifert Plan refers to pauses during working hours. The leave enjoyed by our working people and our progressive intelligentsia is not affected by it."

Kukowa warmed to the subject: "But that is a gap in the Seifert Plan. There must be thousands of working people who would not wish to interrupt their peaceful reconstruction efforts even while on holiday. To them a holiday is merely a uselessly wasted break in their working time. We ought to set up collectives for the constructive utilization of holiday time, colleague Kranich."

Kranich grinned. He thought at last he would be able to trap the elusive Kukowa. "It's not a bad idea. But if I may be permitted a personal question, colleague doctor—would you be prepared to launch the scheme?"

Kukowa dramatically struck his chest. "But of course. This very summer. Socialism needs deeds, colleague Kranich."

Kranich appreciatively pursed his lower lip. "I must congratulate you, colleague doctor. I didn't think you had it in you. We must have another talk about it." More amicably than was his custom, he took his leave to pursue his search of Dr Busch. Kukowa had clearly earned a good mark from him for his 'socialist attitude.'

I rather thought that he had overdone it. Surely Kranich would have a talk with Hansen and learn the whole truth? But Kukowa dismissed the objection. "Let him. To tell the truth, in that conversation I had with Hansen I voluntarily waived my claim to holiday accommodation—needless to say, not until I realized that he was not going to allot me a place anyway. I believe that Hansen will, in his own interest, commend me for my voluntary resignation."

Jürgen Warberg had meanwhile left the room. "You'll end up as a Hero of Socialist Labour yet, Kukowa," I prophesied with a shake of my head.

"Much too strenuous for me," he laughed. "But they'll have to try a lot harder before they can get me down with their tricks."

14

It was time for my afternoon round. I began it in Hansen's ward, accompanied by Warberg. We stopped for a few minutes at the bed of a sixty-six-year-old man, an old-age pensioner.

"We're going to operate on you to-morrow, Herr Schwarze," Dr Warberg said. "Nervous?"

The grey-haired man, who had been an engine-driver until the year before, shook his head. "I went through the artillery barrage of Douaumont in the first war, and I drove trains through partisan-infested territory in the second. What should I be afraid of at my time of life?"

"Any relations?" I asked. He told us about his family, full of pride. "Yes, a son and a daughter. They're both in the West. My wife died four years ago, but I've got a sister who now keeps house for me. She's younger than me, and won't get her old-age pension until next year. I've got to keep alive until then, Herr Oberarzt. We are both living on my old-age pension now. I know you won't tell me that I've got cancer, and really I'd rather not know. But you've just got to keep me alive for another year. I've got a job to do until then."

I looked the old man straight in the eye: "We'll do everything we can for you, Herr Schwarze."

The old-age pensioner had in fact cancer of the rectum. Because his growth was no longer operable Dr Hansen would have to make an artificial orifice from his intestine the following day. Busch and Warberg were down on the operations rota to assist him.

Next morning, before the operation, I ran into Busch in the corridor. He looked pale and tired. His examination as a specialist was in five days' time. Since there was a lot of work to do at the hospital just then, he had to do his revising in the evenings and well into the night.

Busch told me why Paul Kranich had been looking for him the previous afternoon. The Political Director had been promised delivery of two television sets, to be allotted to deserving and reliable members of the hospital staff. True, they had to be paid for in full, but at least they were available without the usual waiting period. Kranich's choice—possibly as a result of a word from Hansen, for whom Busch had lately been doing extra duties—had been Wolfgang Busch and the male nurse Bollmann.

The nurses and Sisters had finished their preparations for the operation. Busch and I parted. He was to assist Hansen during the operation on the old-age pensioner Schwarze, while I, together with Kukowa and Reinfeld, had to do two appendicectomies and a complicated fracture in the theatre next door.

We had just finished the second appendix when Busch burst in on us. "Can you spare a second?" he asked me. "For heaven's sake come back with me. I just can't watch it any longer."

In the theatre next door Hansen was standing by the operating table, cursing that Busch had run away. I took in the situation at a glance. Dr Hansen was engaged on performing a colostomy. He was staring at the wound with glazed eyes. Probably he had been drinking again all night.

"What d'you want, Herr Oberarzt?" he growled at me.

Instead of replying I asked Sister Helga for a pair of sterile gloves and pulled out the transverse part of the large intestine into which the artificial opening should have been cut. This transverse part lay immediately underneath the stomach. But Dr Hansen had cut a hole into the stomach wall and made an artificial stomach orifice. With this wound the old-age pensioner who wanted to live another year would barely have lived another three days.

I did not have to waste any words. The moment I showed Hansen the intact large intestine he realized what he had done. He nodded quickly, picked up needle and suture, and sewed up the slit in the stomach again.

About noon Busch came to see me. He was in despair. "Twice I tried to draw his attention to his incredible blunder," he reported, "but each time he cut me short and ordered me to be silent. I did not understand enough about surgery, he said; I had better pass my specialist's examination first. What was I to do? I couldn't watch the poor man being doomed to a painful death. Now Hansen is going to take it out on me, and may even see that I fail.

It's enough to drive you crazy—to be dependent on such people. Are you going to report the incident?"

"What's the use?" I asked. "The Party isn't going to drop Hansen. What does the Party care about one dead old-age pensioner? I remember the remark of some big noise in the Academy of Sciences: 'In the impending clash between socialism and capitalism so many millions are going to die that a few dozen deaths on the operating table are of no significance.' Maybe I haven't quoted him accurately, but that certainly was the gist of it."

Busch clenched his fists. "You know," he said, "if one sees and hears all this it really is a crime to be the cat's-paw of these people. We are becoming accomplices in everything that is being done here. We are gradually drifting into a situation that we simply can't answer for any longer." And more softly he added: "We ought to go somewhere where a doctor can still be a doctor. If you came along I'd go like a shot."

I put my hands on his shoulders. "Believe me, Wolfgang, I've often thought of this solution during the past few years. To run away—no longer to have the plaster falling into the open wound of some Frau Steinkopf or to watch a colostomy bungled on some old-age pensioner, to be able to start life afresh, free from all ties and considerations. Wonderful! But would you really have an easier conscience? Would you sleep better? You saw this morning how important you are here. Would you seriously have all the good doctors run away and leave the hospital to the Hansens and the Brunkes, to the incompetent and the phrasemongers? What would become of the patients? Schwarze would have died if you had not had the courage to call me. We've got to stay here, Wolfgang, even if it means a sacrifice for us."

The old-age pensioner Schwarze recovered well from his operation. Three days after it he said to me on my round: "Well, I suppose I'm good for another year now. The operation wasn't as bad as Douaumont. Honestly, I wasn't nervous at all. I had every confidence in you doctors. And I was proved right."

"Yes," I repeated after him, "you were proved right." Out of the corner of my eye I shot a glance at Hansen, but he had moved on to the next bed.

15

It was about then that, for the first time, I could not bear the noise of the hospital radio. Perhaps I was overtired and irritable. Perhaps I was also subconsciously rebelling against stomaching any more humiliations. I wanted to listen to a patient's heart sounds in Ward 16. I could not hear anything. The strains of a revolutionary workers' song, played by a brass band, drowned everything. "Don't listen to it," I kept saying to myself, and unwittingly glanced over to the bed where Lola had passed on to me this piece of philosophy. That had been more than two months ago. A whole eternity seemed to have intervened between then and now. At the time I had regarded it as a practicable prescription for survival as a human being in our country. Now I had the impression that I was on the best way to becoming cowed. Did I really have to accept everything that was ordered from above? Even when it was unjustifiable from a medical point of view?

I instructed Sister Eva to ring through to the porter in his glass box by the main entrance and ask him to turn the radio off for a few minutes. I told her to say that I needed absolute quiet for an urgent medical examination.

While Sister Eva was telephoning I again tried to listen to the heart sounds, and I was again unlucky. Eva Schirmer returned simmering with rage. The porter had told her he could not turn off the radio.

I got up, took my reflex hammer from my pocket, and hit the junction box on the wall. The brittle plastic cover shattered. Wires and terminal screws were exposed. Two more vigorous blows and the job was done.

With a pitiful whimper the brass band petered out. The women in the beds were staring at me in horror. Only Granny Novotny grinned delightedly. "There'll never be another peep out of that one," she chuckled.

Breathless silence fell. But the heartbeats which I heard, even before I put my stethoscope on the patient's chest, were my own. There were several articles in our criminal code dealing with the sort of thing I had just done. But I quickly regained my equanimity. Let all the Kranichs the Party could muster come down upon me—I had good medical reasons for what I had done.

The news of my drastic action spread through the hospital like wildfire. And what nobody had thought possible did in fact happen: Paul Kranich passed the incident over in silence. On the following day an electrician appeared in the ward and fixed up the loudspeaker again. After that the whole affair was forgotten.

The radio continued to blare. But we doctors had the impression that the volume had been turned down a little.

A few days later, while I was examining a patient in the men's ward, Sister Anneliese excitedly called me to the telephone. "Long distance from West Berlin, Herr Oberarzt," she whispered to me, since at first I was in no particular hurry to interrupt my examination.

West Berlin? I did not know anyone who would ring me from there. Calls of that nature, as far as I knew, were all channelled through a special exchange in the Federal Republic, and were said to be regularly monitored by the State Security Service. For that reason it was advisable to weigh each word carefully.

I went across to the ward office and picked up the telephone. I recognized Lola's voice at once. "This is one of your patients, Doctor. I am only on a short visit here. Please do not try to get in touch with me during the next few weeks. The doctors who are now treating me insist that I stay at home and take great care of myself. On the few occasions when I do go out they usually accompany me. But it will all blow over, since I am being a very good patient. I shall come and consult you later, but please wait until you hear from me. And don't forget *The Force of Destiny*, Doctor."

Part Three

1

The fields were showing the first touches of green, and in the hedges the first buds appeared. A pale blue sky arched over the town. True, for several weeks a cold wind had been blowing from the east, drying out the land and driving before it clouds of dust such as are usually encountered only in summer. The air was still chilly and inhospitable. But inside the car one already had the illusion of a warm spring day. We had decided to enjoy this sunny Sunday afternoon in late March by driving out into the country-side. Angelica, now sixteen months, had made herself comfortable on the rear seat, and had spread several dolls and a teddy bear about her. My wife sat beside me, peering into the passing landscape for signs of spring, happy at the thought that the long, bleak winter was over. She proudly wore her new grey spring costume, which had only just been finished, even though out of doors she still had to wear her winter coat over it. "This is how I'd like to drive with you for hours on end," Ruth said, leaning her head against my shoulder.

"Always straight on? Until we are in the West?" I asked.

She regarded me lovingly. "Do you really think I would dictate the direction to you? I don't care where we are going, so long as I can sit by your side. You men are such children. Don't you know that I've long reconciled myself to the fact that you must stay here? And I stay wherever you are."

"Even in an attic?"

She laughed. "Even in a rabbit warren, if need be. Do you

remember—six years ago you promised to build me a castle? From old newspapers, perhaps."

"And I wanted to hunt bears," I added, "and return from the chase with the sweetest honey for you."

"And all you have learned from the bear is how to growl," she said teasingly.

"But I've since discovered that you're not so keen on honey as I once thought," I replied on the same note.

Ruth straightened up and ran her hand through my hair. "You know, Jackie," she said pensively, "I don't think it's true that a man comes to know his wife better with the years. You know less of me to-day than you did then. There are a lot of things one learns during the course of married life, but I fear that there is an awful lot that one is in danger of forgetting."

"Are you trying to say that I ought to become a more attentive pupil?" I asked.

"I am trying to say, Peterkin, that we should both try to forget what had best be forgotten. And we should try to hang on to all that's beautiful and be utterly happy again."

I braked and let the car roll to a stop. "Unless this is something I have forgotten in the meantime, all that's beautiful invariably starts with a kiss," I said, and took her in my arms.

We had intended to drive farther into the country. But because Angelica was getting restless, and in her boredom started throwing her dolls over my shoulder at the steering-wheel, we changed our minds and returned towards the town.

At the Waldhaus, a restaurant on the edge of a small wood, we decided to stop for coffee. All the tables in the spacious but ill-kept room were taken. As I was craning my neck, looking for empty seats, somebody waved to me from a corner and pointed to two empty chairs. It was Reinfeld, who had managed to get a table for himself and Ute Weltz. We joined them.

We were packed tight and uncomfortably at the table. Angelica, whom I had kept on my lap to begin with, got impatient and began to toddle about among the tables. The air was heavy with the smell of cheap coffee and cigarette smoke. An iron stove spread an insufferable heat. The wall before me was adorned with a cardboard notice saying 'State retail agency for beer-sausage and bean coffee.' I felt depressed by all this poverty, sordidness, and ugliness.

But Reinfeld and Ute were pleasant company. They were a fine couple, both of them tall and fair, with frank, open faces. They clearly knew what they wanted.

Reinfeld was due to finish his obligatory year as a houseman within a few days. It was unlikely that he would be allowed to stay at the hospital beyond that time. He had been invited to join the People's Army as a doctor.

Angelica readily took to Reinfeld, who was now dandling her on his lap. "We are both fond of children," he confessed, "but we can't get married just yet. With the future as uncertain as it is now one can't saddle oneself with even the most charming wife in the world." He stroked Ute's hand and added: "Besides, we've hardly known one another three months. Some people lose their gall-stones in the operating theatre, but I found a precious stone there. It remains to be seen, of course, if it's genuine."

"It's genuine all right," interjected my wife, who had just been talking to Ute.

We all returned to the town in my car.

2

FRAU MÖSER had a difficult time on Tuesday. The operations had taken longer than usual. As a result, everybody was anxious to get their meal quickly in order to be punctual for the doctors' meeting in the nurses' common-room. Paul Kranich had spoken of nothing for several days past but this discussion with high Party officials. For once there was no need for him to publicize the occasion: we doctors were all anxious to meet the men on whom we depended.

I climbed the stairs with Dr Wolfgang Busch, newly qualified as a surgeon. He had passed his examination the day before. It had been a difficult examination, and two of the five candidates had failed. But Wolfgang's hard work had paid dividends.

We found seats near the front. Professor Brunke and Paul Kranich, our two Directors, were standing in front of the speaker's desk, talking to the three visitors. Thus I had a chance of getting a good look at the officials who held the key positions in our district. They were all three well dressed and well groomed.

I recognized one of them—a tall man, now slightly running to fat, with short, cropped thick grey hair. He was Max Werther, the Deputy Chairman of the Regional Executive of the Socialist Unity Party. I had seen his picture on posters and in the papers. He had a full face, perhaps a little flabby—certainly softer than the currently displayed photographs, but even so reflecting drive and will-power. His eyes were cool and appraising, but not unfriendly. Werther was wearing an elegant grey flannel pin-striped suit and a blue patterned tie with a freshly laundered stylish white collar. If I had encountered Werther in West Germany I should have taken him for a bank manager or big-businessman.

Busch told me that the tall, thin man with the strikingly long nose was Dr Hans Richter, the Chairman of the Regional Executive of the Liberal Democratic Party. Hitherto I had known only his name, which was seen frequently at the end of appeals addressed to the middle class and the intelligentsia. Richter was an unsuccessful solicitor who had been compelled to give up his practice shortly after the War for lack of clients, and who had thereupon devoted all his time to Party politics. He was nervous and excitable, invariably held a cigarette between his long, spidery fingers and talked in jerky sentences.

The third visitor, a short, stocky man with a jovial double chin and fleshy face, must be Eduard Peterich, the Chairman of the National Front in our Region. He tilted his head backward when he spoke to the others, and gave himself an air of keen attention.

Professor Brunke introduced the three officials and then invited Max Werther to address us on the Party's attitude to the intelligentsia. Werther spoke with the voice of a trained orator, clearly and convincingly, with well-placed emphases. We waited in vain for the empty catch-phrases which usually abound in Party political speeches. There was nothing about the fraternal struggle of the creative intelligentsia shoulder to shoulder with the working people for the peaceful building of socialism. There were no attacks against the nuclear armament policy of the capitalist war-mongers. In short, nothing of the jargon which Kukowa imitated so excellently.

Werther spoke of concrete matters. The State, he said, was fully aware of the magnitude and the value of the contribution made by the intelligentsia, and in particular by the medical profession, towards the building of the new democratic order. Throughout his speech he substituted for the usual term 'socialism' the word 'democracy,' as no doubt less offensive to the ears of intellectuals. The State and Party, he went on, were therefore ceaselessly striving to protect the rights of the intelligentsia. We could rely on their support in every respect. The economic security and independence of members of the professions were assured. Doctors were able to work in complete freedom in the German Democratic Republic. There were no restrictions on supplies of necessary medicines. Children whose fathers were members of the intelligentsia were permitted to study at universities. Even though the accommodation shortage continued to be serious as a result of the War, many doctors were assigned good flats under priority schemes. Doctors received interzonal passes without any difficulties, and were also able to travel abroad.

With every sentence the tension grew among the audience. Every one of us had experienced for himself that most of these statements were untrue. Every one of us could refute the Party speaker from his own experience.

"I wonder how he's going to save his face after this?" Busch whispered to me.

"In return," Werther exclaimed in conclusion, "we expect nothing that's unreasonable. We expect from the intelligentsia a loyal attitude and readiness to co-operate in the building of a democratic order."

Throughout the whole speech had run an urgent undertone: Stay here! We will do anything for you because we need you.

Don't go over to the West! The speeches of the other two Party leaders merely re-echoed the words of the powerful man from the Socialist Unity Party. Dr Richter was a little more matter-of-fact and merely enumerated the privileges which doctors were in fact being granted. Thus there was a regulation that a flat vacated by a doctor could be let only to another doctor. Now and again the issue of interzonal passes was indeed temporarily relaxed to enable us to attend medical congresses in West Germany. The purchase of motor-cars was made easier for us doctors. But all these were general regulations, and they were by no means invariably observed in the individual case.

Even for our 'Radish,' our political sycophant Professor Brunke, Werther's speech had been rather strong beer. He was the first to ask to speak in the debate. He announced for a start that he had not received an interzonal pass either for the German Therapeutic Week in Karlsruhe or for the North-West German Medical Congress in Hamburg. A number of indispensable projects for the hospital had not been approved. He even put in a good word for us doctors by pointing out that many of his staff still had no proper flat.

Nearly every one in the audience wanted to speak in the debate, and to relate their own difficulties, which disproved Werther's optimistic picture. The scene was very much the same as during the recent discussion following my lecture. Except that Werther proved a more skilful chairman than Paul Kranich.

After a little while he cut short the debate and mounted the rostrum to reply to the several points made by the speakers. "I am terribly sorry if what you have just reported has actually happened. Needless to say, this has in no way been our intention. If, for instance, Professor Brunke was twice refused an interzonal pass, then these were clearly the mistaken decisions of subordinate officials lacking in understanding. You will appreciate, no doubt, that we can't keep an eye on everything ourselves. What we have told you are the official directives on how the intelligentsia is to be treated. If these directives have not invariably been observed I am exceedingly sorry. I promise you that I will examine all these cases and give you every possible help."

These vague clichés were too much for me. While Werther was clearly getting ready to declare the meeting closed, I leapt to my feet. "We need rather more definite assurances from you, Herr Werther," I called out. In the excitement my voice probably sounded louder than I had intended. The faces that turned towards me reflected shocked surprise. Brunke gave me a reproachful glance. Everything had gone so nicely according to plan, Werther had concluded the meeting on a conciliatory note—and there I was, breaking the rules of the game.

Werther controlled his annoyance and asked with feigned indifference: "Is there anything else you wish to say?"

"Yes," I replied. "We have a great many requests which we must make in the name of our patients. Here are just a few examples from the surgical department: we are made to use instruments which endanger our patients' lives. Our scalpels are frequently badly ground, our needle-holders are worn out, we lack a cholangioscope to look for stones in the gall-duct, our plaster of Paris is heavy and brittle, our suturing material keeps breaking, our anaesthetic ether frequently fails to send our patients to sleep, and we lack many important medicines. If you, Herr Werther, really wish to help us and our patients, then we need a promise which is subsequently kept."

Werther's eyes flashed at me venomously. "Are you suggesting that I am in the habit of breaking my promises?" he asked menacingly.

I replied coolly: "I merely wanted to point out that some changes here are needed badly and urgently."

Comrade Werther left me in no doubt that my criticisms had annoyed him. From then onward he looked straight through me, or turned to the obsequiously nodding Brunke as he spoke of the imminent far-reaching changes in the supply situation. The bottlenecks in the field of medical supplies and medical instruments were well known to the authorities, and everything was being done to reduce them as quickly as possible. Raising his voice, he exclaimed: "You may rest assured, gentlemen, that it is my personal wish, and the wish of my comrades on the Central Committee, to equip our doctors with the best medicines and instruments that can be obtained in the world. It has always been one of our principal demands that everything must be done for the sick, because solicitude for man is at the very centre of our programme."

With this catch-phrase, which we had all heard *ad nauseam* from Paul Kranich, Werther managed some sort of dignified exit for himself after I had spoilt his earlier peroration. But the jarring note which had pervaded the meeting was too obvious to be missed by anyone. The hospital staff returned to their tasks every bit as sceptical as they had been before. The only appeal which the doctors had heard clearly, though it had never been put into words, was: Stay here! Don't go over to the West!

3

I COULD not get the arguments with the Party officials out of my mind for the rest of the day. That evening Busch and I were 'on call.' We sat together in my little office, making tea. Busch was clearly upset: he lit one cigarette after another. "I can't watch all this injustice much longer," he complained. "The shortages of which you reminded Werther are, after all, only one side of the misery that we witness in our wards every day."

Busch crushed an empty cigarette packet and nervously twisted it into a sausage. "There are all the human conflicts as well," he continued. "This afternoon, for instance, a decision was made in my ward which I think quite inexcusable. The day after to-morrow a woman of fifty-five, suffering from multiple sclerosis and a broken leg which refuses to unite, is to be transferred to a State nursing centre for the chronically ill. We need her bed, and there is no hope of helping her by surgical means."

I did not quite see what Busch was getting excited about. Naturally, no patient likes going to a nursing centre, but a surgical ward is not intended for patients who require no surgical treatment. I tried to explain this to him.

He nodded his head. "Of course, there can be no argument about the medical side of the case. But what about the human side? Frau Brinkmann is a business-woman. Her husband is in prison for some fatuous economic offence. He comes out at the end of May—that is, in ten weeks' time. Their children have gone over to the West. If Frau Brinkmann is transferred to the nursing centre now her household will have to be liquidated and her furniture and belongings sold. When her husband comes out of prison he is faced with nothing. His shop is closed, his wife's in a nursing centre, his belongings have been sold, and his flat is occupied by strangers. How can one be a party to this kind of thing?"

Now I too lit a cigarette. I poured out some more tea. Although Busch's ward came under one of the other two senior surgeons in our department, I nevertheless promised him to see if I could do anything for Frau Brinkmann. In one way or another we had to manage things so she could stay in hospital until her husband came out of prison. "You know, Wolfgang," I said, "a doctor in this country is half-way between a dentist and a father confessor. After all, it is a satisfying thought that one can occasionally help people with their mental and material difficulties, and not only with their tummy-aches and broken legs."

"I hope you succeed," Busch remarked sceptically.

4

WE WERE in for a disturbed night. Just as we were going to kip down Nitschke, the male nurse on night duty, rang through. There was a woman with black eyes in Casualty, he said, and rang off. Busch, who took the call, replaced the receiver, shaking his head. "Did you invite a woman with black eyes for this hour of night? Maybe with red hair and dimples on her chin? Let's hope she's sufficiently sorry for herself to give us some excuse to both treat her at once."

Nitschke was not in the habit of playing practical jokes in the middle of the night. While I was still walking down the stairs I could hear a woman talking to him in a strident voice: ". . . and then he shouted at me and called me a bloody bitch. 'You watch your language, Anton,' I said. 'You've been drinking again.' And then I pasted him one because he had no money left on him. And he started screaming and raving and smashed two plates down on the floor in front of me. He'd get a divorce, he kept saying. So I hit him another good one, for that's no language to use to one's wife, Herr Professor."

Nitschke, thus addressed as professor, was unable to get a word in edgeways. "Well, then, as he went on shouting I flung the settee cushion at his head. It's quite a soft cushion, Herr Professor—he can't have felt it at all. But this swine of a man then started hitting me with his fist. Fortunately a traffic cop who heard the noise walked in just then. He sent me over here, because you can never tell what complications might arise with such injuries."

On entering the room I saw a woman of barely thirty, with blue-black contused patches under her eyes. She immediately pounced on me, and no doubt was prepared to tell me the whole story from the start. I stopped her with a gesture, quickly examined her, and prescribed aluminium acetate compresses.

"D'you think your husband might become violent again when you get home?" I asked, just to be on the safe side.

"He'd better not try, the drunken swine!" she said threateningly. "And how many days' sick leave are you going to give me, Herr Doktor?" She was most annoyed when I told her that she could go back to work. "There one goes trudging all through the night to get to the hospital and they don't even give you sick leave. The State's doing everything for the doctors—and what are the doctors doing for the workers? Damn-all!"

I left her alone with her logic and instructed Nitschke to see her out.

"For a father confessor you did not over-sympathize with the wife of a drunkard," Busch mocked.

Two hours later we were called again. A police car had brought in two drunk policemen. While off duty at their barracks they had started a fight; a window-pane had been smashed, and one of the men had suffered injuries to his face and hands. Some of the cuts were deep, and bleeding freely. The other had broken a finger while hitting his colleague with his fist. Both of them were noisy and unruly, and refused to be treated by us. They grabbed hold of Nitschke and struck out wildly at Busch and myself. It was impossible to bandage them. I therefore telephoned the riot police and asked them to collect the two men. The duty officer at the other end, however, shied away from the idea the moment I told him that our drunk and disorderly customers were policemen.

"What kind of uniform are they wearing?" he asked.

"Navy blue, with light blue flashes on their collars and epaulettes."

"Oh, traffic police. In that case we'd rather not get involved. We'll notify their unit, and they can collect their own men."

The traffic police form a separate division within the police force. They correspond to the former railway police, and live in barracks. We left the two drunks alone in the waiting-room, and confined ourselves to keeping an eye on them. Nitschke likewise had no desire to get involved in a tussle with them. He could still feel the bruise where a drunk had kicked him a few weeks previously.

Before long a party of ten sturdy policemen arrived in a lorry and collected their fighting-cocks. Presumably some police surgeon attended to their wounds later. For any other doctor it would have been inadvisable to use force against the police—especially when even the riot police were reluctant to act against another police unit.

"What a shambles it all is!" Busch cursed. "I can't stand it much longer."

Always the same threat. Busch's nerves seemed to have suffered somewhat from all the work he had put in for his specialist's examination.

5

"Until the end of May?" Professor Zöllinger, my chief, asked when I had quite openly told him about the case of Frau Brinkmann.

"Yes—her husband comes out of prison in ten weeks' time."

Professor Zöllinger wrinkled his leathery brow. "It is not our job to help an offender and an enemy of the State," he then said with emphasis. "A patient who merely needs nursing must of course be passed on to a nursing centre. But I'm by no means satisfied that in the case of Frau Brinkmann some surgery might not perhaps be necessary after all. Have you got a vacant bed in one of your wards as from to-morrow?"

"I could discharge a patient from Ward 16."

"Excellent," the chief said. "You take over the case and carry out another thorough examination of the patient."

It was a generous gesture on Professor Zöllinger's part. It was clothed in unchallengeable propriety, while showing human sympathy for a case of special hardship.

For the time being Frau Brinkmann's home was safe. It was now up to me to find a credible justification for her continued detention in hospital. Busch, who assisted me with my operations that morning because Reinfeld had been summoned to report to the Regional Medical Officer, was overjoyed. "All we need now is a lot of bright ideas in order to draw out Frau Brinkmann's treatment until the end of May," I said to him. Well, we were not going to run out of ideas.

Ute Weltz, who was again in charge of the anaesthetic, seemed jumpy and abstracted that morning. She was worried about Reinfeld. His interview with the Regional Medical Officer would decide whether he could stay with us or not. About lunch-time Reinfeld returned, fairly optimistic. Several other young housemen who had just finished their first year in hospital had been summoned to the Regional Medical Officer together with him.

There an officer of the People's Army and an official of the Wismut-AG in Aue—the East German uranium-mining enterprise—had been waiting for them. Dr Tschauner, the Regional Medical Officer, had reminded them that they owed to the State the privilege of being doctors. Now he, the Regional Medical Officer, expected them to show their gratitude to the State. He had therefore arranged for them to hear first-hand details about service in the People's Army Medical Corps or as an industrial medical officer in Aue. The officer and the mining official had then tried to persuade the young doctors to apply for service with them.

Reinfeld, it appeared, had skilfully avoided committing himself. He had promised nothing and signed nothing. He was now hoping that perhaps he might be permitted to stay at our hospital.

Ute flung her arms round his neck, notwithstanding all the doctors and Sisters present in the corridor.

6

DR HANSEN had somehow worked out that he was still entitled to a fortnight's leave. I do not know what mathematical jugglery he had resorted to—but the chief was unable to refute his contention. He merely succeeded in persuading Hansen to postpone his leave by ten days, as we were hoping to get a new assistant doctor at the beginning of April.

Eva Schirmer and Ernst Pfeifer, whose socialist wedding was due to take place that Friday, were delighted with this development. The news that their patron intended to leave the day before their wedding had greatly alarmed them. Hansen had promised them a magnificent wedding. Four trees in tubs were to be brought by lorry and placed on either side of the table behind which the registrar was to sit. Floral decorations were to be bought, as well as a silk dress for the bride and a new suit for the groom. Hansen himself was to deliver a festive speech about the meaning of a socialist wedding. He had promised to provide a wedding feast at a long, flower-decorated table, for at least twenty guests, in addition to the couple's friends from among the hospital staff. Needless to say, he was also going to make sure that adequate quantities of drink were available. Finally, Hansen had arranged for a daily paper to send a photographer.

On Thursday morning, however, he announced that he had bad news. The kitty of the trade-union committee had proved to be empty. The only person he had invited was the registrar.

Sister Eva burst into tears. Ernst Pfeifer looked helpless. Nobody knew what to do.

To make matters worse, Dr Hansen had also suddenly discovered that he was no orator. He came to see me at my office, paid me a few belated compliments on my excellent lecture about accident prevention, and declared emphatically that I was the best speaker in the hospital, and must therefore make the speech at the wedding. I was disinclined to lend my support to the institution of a socialist wedding, an institution deliberately designed as an affront to a wedding in church. I coldly declined his invitation.

In the lunch-break Hansen came over to my department. He was exuberant as a schoolboy, and tweaked Eva's chin. "Chin up, you silly girl," he said playfully. "Everything's arranged. Surely you didn't doubt my good intentions?" Turning to me, he added: "Herr Oberarzt, may I ask you to support me now? I want to go and plead for our dear Sister Eva, that indispensable member of your department."

I followed Hansen across the courtyard to where Professor Brunke had just started one of his voluntary reconstruction shifts. Hanson apologized for disturbing him: we had come, he explained, on a matter of extraordinary importance for the hospital.

Brunke rested his weight on the spade and asked: "Yes, I remember—what's happening about that socialist wedding?"

"Everything's arranged, Herr Professor," Hansen boasted. "Just a few details which want settling. We're still looking for someone to make the festive speech."

"Don't look at me," Brunke protested.

"No, indeed, we should hardly presume to trespass on your valuable time," Hansen said obsequiously. "But there are also a few expenses that have yet to be met."

"Minor sums?"

"But of course, Herr Professor. Quite minor sums."

"How much is there outstanding, Herr Hansen?"

I was watching Hansen out of the corner of my eye. He was fidgeting with his tie. "Well, that is to say, there are first of all the flowers. Then there is the bride's dress. . . . And a suit for colleague Pfeifer. And we haven't got the money for the food either."

Brunke blanched. "You mean that all the trade-union committee is paying for is the drinks?"

Hansen wriggled like an eel. "Yes—that's to say—we can cut out the drinks, or cut them down considerably. Besides, there's really no need for wine. . . ."

"Stop prevaricating, man," Brunke exploded. "Are you saying that the trade unions are not contributing anything at all?"

Hansen helplessly spread out his arms. "Unfortunately, there's no money in the kitty, Herr Professor. That's why we've come to you; we were hoping . . ."

He kept saying 'we' and acting altogether as if I was one of those responsible for the trade-union committee's lack of funds.

Brunke angrily flung down his spade and asked us to accompany him to his office. His secretary, who was on the point of calling him, about-turned in the doorway of the Medical Department. Her mission had become unnecessary.

After a great deal of haggling Brunke eventually authorized two bunches of flowers for the registrar's table and a simple meal for the bridal couple and the witnesses. Everything else was cut out. But at least the first socialist wedding in the hospital had been saved.

It turned out to be one of the saddest weddings that I have ever been to. Eva Schirmer arrived with eyes red from crying. She wore a faded summer frock, the best she had. Ernst Pfeifer looked uncomfortable in a blue serge suit that had become too tight for him. The registrar's table was covered with the red cloth which normally adorned Paul Kranich's peace corner. Down the front of the table hung the black, red, and gold national flag with hammer and compasses. The nurses' common-room was less than half full.

After the rather pedestrian ceremony, which ended with the presentation of the 'Book of the Family' to the newly married couple, Paul Kranich stepped forward and delivered a speech which he himself described as solemn. He had undertaken the task at the very last moment. Hansen had not dared after all to have the shabby ceremony immortalized by photographs. Not even a brief notice appeared in the local paper on the following day. I might add that this remained the only socialist wedding ever to take place in our hospital.

7

DR HANSEN was busy getting ready for his leave. Because of these arduous activities he was seen at the hospital even less frequently than usual. For a fortnight his ward had to be looked after by the 'living corpse.' Moreover, Hansen needed a stand-in for his supplementary job of Medical Officer to the People's Police. He succeeded in persuading the good-natured Wolfgang Busch to take on his duties there for the time being. Busch had been with the police at one time, and was therefore a more obvious choice than any of the other doctors.

This sideline of his—his work for the People's Police—was highly profitable to Hansen in more ways than one. It is always a good thing in our country to maintain good relations with the police. They are a valuable insurance in critical situations, just as are connexions with senior Party officials. Hansen had taken care to reinsure himself with both organizations against the ever-present dangers of political disfavour.

Moreover, he derived from his work advantages which were not even enjoyed by senior Party officials. Hansen's duties with the People's Police involved the medical supervision of prisoners. In this way he had managed to get a gang of prisoners to maintain and repair his house. For several days the convicts had arrived with building materials from prison stocks and renovated Hansen's house from top to bottom. Hansen had somehow succeeded in gaining possession of this house, which used to belong to a dentist who had escaped to the West, without having to pay a penny for it. He was living in greater comfort than our chief. How he arranged these things was a mystery to us.

The work which Busch now undertook for a fortnight was mainly in the prison for criminal offenders. But if some political prisoner fell ill he had to drive over to the jail of the State Security Service. Both institutions were in the city centre, not far from each other. Busch did not exactly enjoy this spare-time activity, but in his good-natured way he always found it difficult to turn down Hansen's requests. Besides, Hansen had found ways and means, while Busch was preparing for his specialist's examination, of persuading his younger colleague to do odd little jobs for him.

I did not think we should miss Hansen greatly at the hospital. Just then, however—while he was still getting ready for his leave— an event occurred which was to leave a painful gap in our under- staffed hospital establishment. True, we had expected that Reinfeld would have to do his second obligatory year as a houseman at some other hospital—but in the event the loss was greater than we had anticipated.

One morning, just before we started operating, Reinfeld showed me a letter. It was from the People's Army, informing him that his verbal application, made in the presence of the Regional Medical Officer, had been accepted. He was now to support this by formal written application at his earliest convenience, and hold himself ready to start service in the People's Army.

"I never applied for any such service," Reinfeld assured me. "It's either a misunderstanding or pure bluff. The Regional Medical Officer will bear me out. They're not going to catch me in this clumsy fashion."

I allowed him to take the afternoon off so that he could go and see Dr Tschauner, the Regional Medical Officer. Reinfeld was back within an hour. The Regional Medical Officer had not even seen him. He had sent word through his secretary that he was in conference, and that in any event he was unable to remember all the details of the recent interview. He had not been personally acquainted with any of the young housemen, and was therefore unable to say which of them had and which had not applied for service with the People's Army. An official in the Regional Medical Officer's department had then advised Reinfeld to do his honourable service as a doctor in the People's Army. According to Reinfeld, the man's argument had been something like this: "Surely it is quite irrelevant whether you did or did not apply verbally. The point is that you cannot now shirk this honourable service, and must therefore submit your written application as soon as possible."

"And what are you going to do now?" I asked Reinfeld.

He calmly shrugged his shoulders. "What choice have I, Herr Oberarzt?" These were the last words he ever spoke to me. On the following morning neither he nor Ute Weltz turned up for duty. I sent someone to look for them in their respective rooms on the second floor, but there was no trace of them. Their clothes were hanging in the wardrobes, underwear was tidily stowed away in the drawers, pieces of personal belongings and toilet articles were in their proper places.

"Do you suppose they've skipped the country?" Sister Helga was the first to voice our thoughts.

Bollmann, the male nurse, vigorously shook his head. "A regular fellow does not skedaddle just because he's got to put on a uniform. When I remember my time with the parachutists . . ."

Even Frau Gummer ruled out the idea of escape. Although she had frequently quarrelled with Reinfeld, and although she disliked Ute Weltz if only because of her youth and good looks, she immediately championed them both. "They're in love and they've got to part in a few days' time," was her explanation. "Who can blame them if they want to hide out somewhere overnight, where nobody knows them? And maybe they've missed the first train back."

It sounded very reasonable. I was merely surprised that Frau

Gummer should have hit upon this solution—that querulous and perpetually mistrustful little trade-union official. For the time being she refused to report the disappearance of the two.

I was very glad of her attitude. It gave Reinfeld and Ute a good start in case they had not yet crossed the sector boundary. That this was, in fact, Frau Gummer's intention I did not know until very much later, when I realized what a magnificent actress that woman was.

Three days later came a postcard from Ute Weltz and Horst Reinfeld. The postmark was West Berlin.

8

DURING the next few days Kukowa and I had to look after Reinfeld's wards as well as our own. As a result I arrived about half an hour late for my surgery at the Fortschritt works. The waiting-room was crowded with patients. The first whom Sister Suzanne pushed through the door was a man in a dark blue overall who had only arrived while I was parking my car. He was Alfred Fritsche, the head of the factory militia. I had treated him a few times before. He had an emaciated face, sparse hair, bushy eyebrows, and an unhealthy sallow complexion. Alfred Fritsche was one of those workers who had long ago turned Communist from conviction, but who, because of their intellectual limitations, had made only a modest career. He was a decent old man, much too honest to be picked for some desk job in a Party office. So he had been made head of the factory's team of watchmen, who consisted predominantly of old-age pensioners. In addition he had been charged with the leadership of the factory's Workers' Militia, in spite of his fifty-eight years. It was in the uniform of that force— blue overalls, with a red bar on the sleeve which marked him out as the leader, a leather shoulder-strap, and a navy-blue peaked cap—that he now stood before me.

"I've not come to see you as a patient, Herr Doktor," he said. "I merely wanted to ask you a favour."

He explained that he intended to organize a sports day with his militia, and wanted me to examine his two hundred men with a view to ascertaining their physical fitness.

"A sports day? Is that part of the duties of your militia?" I asked in surprise.

Alfred regarded me guilelessly. "Strictly speaking, no," he confessed. "But we've got to do something to keep the people interested. We've got a lot of tepid and half-hearted members, and some of them are getting bored with the whole business. A sports day would get people enthusiastic again."

These militia groups had been set up with a great deal of propaganda accompaniment in all major industrial enterprises. Workmen and office staff had been persuaded, or sometimes bullied, into joining. The Party's idea was that these groups should be a kind of factory guard in the event of disturbances, and should act as partisans in case of war. Now and again the men were made to turn out on Sundays for all kinds of ridiculous tactical exercises in the field. Anyone driving through the countryside on a Sunday can see these weekend soldiers on the outskirts of towns and industrial centres, padding along roadside ditches or defending some patch of woodland with miniature rifles. Considering that a man like Alfred Fritsche, who had never been in the Army, acted the supreme warlord on those occasions, I could well imagine the enthusiasm of his men for this way of spending their day off.

I rather liked Alfred Fritsche, but I had no intention of breathing new life into the moribund militia of our factory.

The militia leader no doubt sensed my hesitation. He was looking for some way of lending greater emphasis to his request.

"To tell you the truth, Herr Doktor," he said openly, "that idea of a sports day didn't originate with me. It was thought up by our manager, the National Prize winner. If you don't examine my men he'll say that I have failed in my task. He may even get me the sack. As it is, he thinks that I'm not up to my job. He always blames me for the fact that the men are browned off."

I was sorry for Fritsche. "Very well," I said. "I'll examine your men. But you've got to be patient. One of my staff at the hospital is about to go on leave; another has skipped the country. I can barely keep up with my current work."

"Yes, that's how it is," he said pensively. "The young people have no confidence in our State. My only son has also gone to the West. There you spend your life working for the cause, you educate your children in the spirit of socialism, and the moment they're fledged they betray our idea. Surely there's something wrong somewhere, Herr Doktor."

"Yes," I repeated. "There's something wrong somewhere."

Fritsche was unhappy about being put off. He now had to postpone the date of his sports day, since there was no prospect of finding another doctor.

Later in the afternoon it suddenly occurred to me that I could no longer expect much help from the works manager in my search for a flat. I therefore decided to tackle Bollmann again the following morning and see if I could get somewhere with his housing sub-committee.

Bollmann looked at me in surprise. "I'm no longer in charge of the sub-committee," he grunted. "That job was nothing but annoyance, envy, and backbiting. It's only when you've got a job like that that you realize the downright wickedness of people. No—that's no job for an honest ex-parachutist."

If only I had paid more attention to hospital gossip I should have been spared my surprise at Bollmann's decision, as well as at his philosophy about man's wickedness. I discovered from Sister Eva what had caused the male nurse to become such a misanthropist. During the twelve months that he was its chairman Bollmann's sub-committee had allotted six flats to members of the hospital staff. They had all been flats in old buildings, some of them in extremely poor condition. A week before the Housing Office had at last assigned to the hospital a flat in a brand-new block. The sub-committee had met and adopted the remarkable decision that the most deserving applicant for the flat was the sub-committee's chairman himself. Even before this decision became generally known Bollmann had moved in. He even waived his right to a day off, to which he would have been entitled for his removal, in order, as he put it, to save his colleagues any extra work.

By the time the rest of the trade-union committee heard about the allocation of the flat Bollmann had long settled in. There was a really big row on the committee, but no power in the world could dislodge Bollmann from his newly acquired flat. He dismissed all accusations as mere envy and malice, and grandly resigned the post which, now that he had attained his end, was of no more use to him. Until Hansen's return, I was informed, no new chairman would be appointed to the housing sub-committee.

9

ON FRIDAY I got home earlier than usual. Ruth had opened the windows of our attic, and the mild, fragrant April air was wafting in. "The flat's bigger when the windows are open," she joked. "Don't you think so?" Nevertheless, in spite of our thus enlarged apartment we decided to go out after supper. At the end of a lengthy walk we found ourselves outside Busch's flat. Wolfgang Busch and I had seen little of each other during the preceding week. Because of his specialist's examination we had suspended our mutual evening visits some weeks ago. Ruth and I suddenly felt we should like to drop in on Wolfgang Busch and his wife, Helga.

We had to ring twice before the door was opened. Then Wolfgang appeared in the doorway, sweating and panting. "If you wouldn't mind waiting a moment?" he asked. "Helga is just dressing."

We waited patiently. After a little while Wolfgang returned. "We're all at sixes and sevens to-day. We are off to spend the weekend with friends in the country, and are just packing what few things we need."

The elegant three-roomed flat on the first floor of a comfortable house built in the nineties was not as neat and tidy as Helga liked to have it. Bits of paper and pieces of underwear lay here and there; two large trunks stood in a corner. The table was covered with old newspapers and periodicals. Wolfgang produced a bottle of brandy and went to fetch some glasses. A moment later Helga came in from the bedroom. She was wearing a light grey skirt and a pale blue sweater. She was blonde, slim, and delicately built, a pretty and vivacious woman. That evening, however, she seemed a little pale and absent-minded.

Wolfgang was telling me about his work at the prison. "By the way, I've got bad news about the merchant Brinkmann," he said. "I was treating a prisoner to-day who'd shared a cell with him. He told me Brinkmann had been taken away a few days ago and had not been brought back. There is a rumour that he is being questioned about some political offence as well. He is believed to be at the prison of the State Security Service. I've got to go there on Monday anyway, so I'll see if I can find him then."

I tried to dissuade him. Even a doctor is forbidden to talk to political prisoners unless they have reported sick. And even then the conversation must remain confined to medical issues. Hansen had told me so several times.

"I'll be careful," Wolfgang reassured me. "But if the rumour turns out to be true it seems unlikely that Brinkmann will be discharged at the end of May. In which case we'll find it almost impossible to save his wife from being transferred to the nursing centre."

It was difficult enough to keep her at the hospital as it was. I had prescribed an extensive series of X-rays, I had taken a number of blood tests, I had examined her heart and circulation, and I had set into motion a whole series of laboratory tests. If the worst came to the worst I was even prepared to perform some slight operation on her for some unimportant condition. But now it looked as though we might have to give up all hope.

"It's a good thing Hansen is coming back soon," Wolfgang continued. "This prison service isn't doing my nerves any good. Things are worse at the State Security Service. I'm not allowed to talk about what I see there—but I can tell you one thing: in this

123

country of ours we are living a great deal more dangerously than we suspect. A State which trusts its citizens so little does not deserve any trust itself."

"Can't you at least switch on the wireless, Wolfgang, if you must make speeches like this?" Helga cut in anxiously.

"A man's got to speak his mind some time," Wolfgang grumbled, "even if I've got to confine my remarks to my best friend."

A few days later I was to discover that he had kept the most important piece of information even from his best friend. I understood his reasons, and respected them. He had done so only to spare me from knowing things which might be dangerous.

When I met Wolfgang again on Monday night he was very depressed. Everything that he had intended to do had gone wrong. When he got to the civil prison he was told that a political prisoner had reported sick. Here then was his opportunity to enter the prison of the State Security Service. A warder took him to a solitary cell and remained standing by the door. The patient, a fat man with dewlaps, a bald head, and a pot-belly, was lying apathetically on his bunk. Clearly he was feverish. Wolfgang Busch asked him about his pains, examined him, and heard in his chest the rattle and crackle that is typical of incipient pneumonia.

"This man's got to be transferred to the hospital at once," he said to the warder by the door. "Find out if they've got room for him."

The warder went out. Wolfgang seized on this opportunity to ask the sick man if a merchant named Brinkmann had been brought in during the past few days. The sick man did not know. But he had heard that two new men had arrived, and had been put into the cells near the end of the corridor. This at least was a start. Perhaps he could find some pretext for being allowed into these cells.

The warder returned and requested Wolfgang to follow him. Asked whether a bed was available in the prison hospital, he nodded silently. Then he took Wolfgang to a room where an officer was sitting behind a desk. He was told to sit down. A moment later two gentlemen in civilian clothes entered from the next room. The officer politely but very firmly informed Busch that he had just transgressed the boundaries of his medical duties. His conversation with the patient had been listened in to. He was given a formal warning in front of the two witnesses. Any further attempt to learn details about individual prisoners would have to be viewed as an action hostile to the State.

After that Busch was allowed to leave. He returned to the police prison, and there ran into a fellow-doctor who was in charge of the sick bay at the People's Police barracks. Busch knew him from the days when he himself had been a part-time police medical officer. He confided to his colleague what had just happened to him, and described to him his unsuccessful search for the husband of one of our patients. The other man shook his head over Busch's foolishness. "You've been going about this business in quite the wrong way," he said. "No one in his senses plays detective within the Security Service's own territory. But if your man was first found guilty of an economic offence he must have been in the police prison. And information about ordinary criminals is available without any difficulty."

He took Busch over to the administrative office and asked the man in charge of records to look through his files. That man soon confirmed that Brinkmann, Bruno, independent merchant, had been inside for an economic offence. But he had since been transferred elsewhere because of some additional offence. More than that he could not say.

All this Busch told me on Monday evening. "This is the tragic end of this unlucky couple's marriage," he added. "I am very grateful to you for having tried to save the Brinkmanns' home. Now you can let the woman be transferred to the nursing centre."

I warned Busch to be more careful in future. It seemed likely that the State Security Service would keep an eye on a man who had shown such interest in a political detainee.

"You may rely upon me," he said, putting his hand on my shoulder. "I shan't do any more foolish things."

10

THE following day, at lunch-time, Professor Zöllinger asked all doctors of the hospital to come round to his room. As we filed through the door we saw a smart young woman by his side. She wore a light-coloured spring costume, a gay little hat, and shoes with stiletto heels. Her attractive and still youthfully fresh face had been subjected, quite unnecessarily, to an excessive application of lipstick and eyebrow pencil. I thought she might be a visitor from some West German town—and not from one of its best neighbourhoods either.

"I should like to present to you a new colleague of ours," Zöllinger began. I thought I had not heard correctly. I had never seen a woman doctor made up in this cheap way.

Kukowa whispered into my ear: "A symphony in red."

"This young lady," Zöllinger continued after a short pause, "is Fräulein Dr Ellen Tschauner, the daughter of our Regional Medical Officer. She has just qualified, and is going to do her first year as a houseman with us."

Kukowa was the first to recover. "I see it now—the exact image of her father!" he exclaimed with a broad grin. The girl no doubt took it as a compliment, and nodded gratefully.

The pampered young lady did not turn out to be a great deal of help. That much we realized after the first few days. Dr Ellen Tschauner acted the onlooker. Whenever we gave her some easy task she would say with an ingenuous smile: "But I haven't had enough experience to do that."

Even the first operation that she watched the next morning soon began to bore her. Before I could stop her she had left the theatre and lit a cigarette in the corridor outside. As bad luck would have it she ran straight into Professor Brunke, who had just been to see our chief in his laboratory. Brunke was a regular visitor at the Regional Medical Officer's home, and had known his daughter for many years. He took her along to his department and got Dr

Pollak to show her the hospital's showpiece, the sleep-treatment ward. She did not like the anaemic Pollak, and the inspection of the ward bored her even more than our operation.

We were making slow headway that morning because Dr Wolfgang Busch had reported sick. At lunch-time Zöllinger had me called to his office. He had received a letter from Busch and wanted to read it to me.

My dear Herr Professor [Busch had written], unfortunately I shall be unable to turn up at the hospital in the foreseeable future. Symptoms of circulation trouble and a general faintness of heart have begun to show themselves in me lately. An accurate diagnosis is not yet possible since my case, in a manner of speaking, is a borderline one.

The chief regarded me stonily. "Go and look him up at his flat to-night. I am worried about Busch."

Needless to say, he knew as well as I what the letter meant. He was perplexed and shocked. It is always a cause of pain and bitterness when a colleague leaves, deserting his team. And it always gives rise to renewed doubts as to who is acting correctly—the refugee who cannot bear conditions in our country any longer, or we who are determined to stay and to survive the dictatorship.

The only one to condemn Busch was Paul Kranich, when he was opening his Party political training class that afternoon: "An ungrateful man, that Dr Busch. And only recently I got him a television set. . . ."

11

IN THE evening Ruth asked me what was going to happen about Busch's flat now. Good heavens, I had never thought of that. Under the existing regulations the vacated flat of a doctor could be re-let only to a doctor. Much to Frau Möser's annoyance, I went without lunch the following day, and as soon as I had finished my list of operations drove out to the Health Department of the Municipal Administration. The District Medical Officer received me behind his desk, chewing his usual cigar-stub and listening to me with only half an ear. Naturally, he said, I could rely entirely on him. True, there were some other applicants, but if he had to decide the issue he would certainly assign the flat to me. Unfortunately, however, the decision was not with him but with the Housing Office, and all he could do was recommend me. The only upshot of my interview was a piece of free advice: "Drive over at once to the Municipal Housing Office and have your name put down as an applicant. If you're lucky they'll give you the key to the flat straight away."

By then I was feeling murderous. If the District Medical Officer was not prepared to throw in the whole weight of his authority with the Housing Office, what chances had I, as an individual whose deserts for the Worker and Peasant State were exceedingly limited, to say the least, and who did not even wear a Party badge on his lapel? Sure enough, when I got there the answer of the official in charge was almost literally what I had expected: "We've put your name down as a doctor in search of a flat, and as a doctor you are entitled to priority. At the same time, we have on our lists several doctors with higher priority, and naturally we must deal with them first. You will hear from us when we have a flat to assign to you."

At that moment some psychological safety-valve blew inside me. We all walk about with these mental safety-valves which allow us to think treasonable thoughts, but as a rule prevent us from putting them into words. After all, a single wrong word may mean arrest and prison in our country. I brought down my fist on the table and shouted: "If I don't get this flat I'll go to the West." Two officials at neighbouring tables bent their heads lower over their papers. My interlocutor looked at me in startled silence. In his buttonhole he wore the Party badge. He looked depressed and down-at-heel.

After a moment's silence he rose and said a few noncommittal words. He would see what could be done; he would certainly do everything in his power to meet my request. The decision would not be made for a few days, and I should have to be patient until then. After all, it was not up to him alone to decide to whom the flat should go.

I felt suddenly sorry for the little official. He too was no more than a minute cog in the all-powerful machine. What could he have done if some Meritorious People's Doctor had suddenly laid claim to the flat, or if some directive had come down from the Regional Medical Officer, the Regional Party Committee, the National Front, the Free German Trade Union Federation, or any one of the numerous seats of power? Who would have then paid the slightest heed to his recommendation that the flat should go to some obscure *Oberarzt* who was not even a Party member, who did not enjoy the full support of the District Medical Officer, and whose case was not championed by any Meritorious People's Doctor or any important official?

An important official! Just a moment—maybe perhaps a National Prize winner? But unfortunately I had crossed that very man a few days ago by upsetting his plans for a works militia sports day. If the works manager was at all vindictive he could now, with every justification, plead that he was too busy to deal with my request.

Nevertheless, I drove out to the Fortschritt factory. The works manager was in conference with various trade-union officials. I had to wait a quarter of an hour before he emerged by chance into his outer office. As soon as he saw me he asked what I had come for. "A flat?" he exclaimed. "That's a thing that wants seeing to at once. Comrades, we can continue our discussion the day after to-morrow. I've got to see about a flat for our works doctor."

The comrades seemed to accept readily the proposition that a flat for the works doctor was adequate grounds for suspending a meeting. Even a National Prize winner cannot, in our country, get a flat for the mere asking. He ordered his official car to be driven round at once. "You go back to your hospital," he said to me. "I'll let you know."

When I got home in the evening Ruth was in an orgy of planning. In her mind she was already furnishing Busch's flat with our furniture. She just could not understand why I had not got the flat there and then. With feminine logic, she had assumed that as friends of Busch we enjoyed a kind of natural right to the flat. Surely in any other country we should have come to an arrangement with the last tenant and probably got the keys from him? But here, of course, there must not be the slightest suggestion that we had known anything in advance about Busch's escape. Besides, any agreement with him would have been invalid in law once Busch had committed the criminal offence of flight from the Republic.

"Aren't you superstitious?" I asked Ruth. "You oughtn't to count your chickens before they're hatched."

She laughed at me, entirely carefree. "But you'll manage it all right, Jackie! You're such a clever man!"

"I'm a man without a Party card," I reminded her.

She refused to let me damp her optimism. "I shan't be too miserable even if it doesn't work out. So long as you're here, even this attic is a cosy home."

12

ON THE following morning the works manager rang through to congratulate me on my new flat. Over the telephone he gave me a full account of the battle he had fought for me. At the Housing Office things had been easy enough, since he was not only a National Prize winner but also—which was news to me—a member of the Municipal Council. He simply claimed the vacated doctor's flat for the works doctor of the Fortschritt factory. With this move he overrode whatever priority the other doctors on the waiting-list might have enjoyed. State-owned factories had to be given preferential treatment; National Prize winners must not be displeased; a Municipal Councillor might be very useful to the Housing Office staff some day. The works manager was therefore handed the key, and formally signed the acceptance for the flat complete with contents. The furniture and effects, under the existing regulations, had to be 'sold' to the workers of the factory.

As the works manager was about to break the police seal at the front door a young man suddenly raced up the stairs behind him. He introduced himself as a doctor from some hospital, and from his pocket produced a letter to the effect that his trade-union housing sub-committee had assigned the flat to him. The works manager refused to discuss the matter, but the young doctor snatched the key from him and tried to send the old man packing. The manager chuckled loudly into the telephone as he continued his account. "Don't let anyone tell you that an old spinning-works operative is no longer good for a fight," he was crowing delightedly. "I gave that young man the hiding of his life. I took the key away from him and told him if he did not push off at once I'd throw him down the stairs. After that he went off quite meekly. The Fortschritt works came out tops, colleague doctor!"

For the time being, however, we were not yet able to move in. First of all, Busch's furniture had to be 'sold.' This was done in the following way. The factory management had to price the individual items. These prices, as is customary in all such cases, were fixed deliberately low. The television set, a suite of chairs, and two carpets were put down on the list at bargain prices. As a result, customers were instantly found for these valuable items among the officials who had fixed the prices. The works manager chose a few pieces for himself; then the other officials had their turn. Alfred Fritsche, the leader of the militia, also secured a wardrobe. After a fortnight the more valuable effects had all been collected. Once they were out of the flat the factory management acted in strict accordance with the official directives and offered the remaining effects to the shop-floor workers. Altogether five weeks elapsed before the flat was empty, since for a very long time no buyers could be found for an ancient settee, some wobbly kitchen stools, and a woodworm-infested chest of drawers. Not until the latter part of May could we move into our new flat.

13

A few days after Wolfgang Busch's flight yet another household was dissolved. In Wilhelm Pieck Street the People's Police sealed up the flat of Bruno Brinkmann, merchant. With a heavy heart I had signed Frau Brinkmann's transfer papers to a nursing centre. The news had come as a shock to the plucky woman. She had begun to draw new hope as soon as she noticed that we were trying to help her. At first she had been merely frightened of the nursing centre as such, of an indefinite stay in an impersonal atmosphere. Before long she had learned from other patients that her household would be dissolved once she was transferred to a centre. That was when she realized why we were trying to keep her at the hospital. Her confidence in us had grown to such an extent that she thought it impossible that we might have to let her down one day.

I tried hard to break the news to her gently. "The examinations have all turned out very satisfactorily, Frau Brinkmann," I said. "There's no need for any operation. Indeed, we can even spare you the hustle and bustle of the hospital atmosphere. You can now get treatment, until you're quite well again, at one of our centres."

She stared at me as if I had read out her death sentence. Her eyes, which remained absolutely dry, lost their lustre. For several minutes she sat silent, white as chalk.

Granny Novotny, who took pride in being the veteran of the ward, now took up the cudgels for her. "I've been here a very long time, Herr Oberarzt. Why not send me to the nursing centre, then you get an empty bed. But keep Frau Brinkmann here till next month. When her husband comes out of prison he can look after her better at home."

Good old Granny Novotny. She too was prepared to make a sacrifice for her neighbour. Only I was the hard-hearted, unsympathetic doctor who had no understanding for human problems.

In a brittle voice, Frau Brinkmann asked: "What's happened to that nice cheerful plump doctor who used to treat me?"

"Dr Busch has taken a post at another hospital," I explained.

"So that's it . . ." she said slowly. At that moment Ellen Tschauner entered the ward, garishly made up. She had been told to help me in my department in order to enable me temporarily to keep an eye on Reinfeld's wards. She had heard the last few sentences of our conversation, and now plunged in herself: "Why should you dislike the idea of a nursing centre so much, my dear woman? The State pays the bills; you've no worries at all. You really couldn't be better off."

I rounded on her sharply. "Would you mind keeping your ideas to yourself, Fräulein Dr Tschauner, while I'm talking to my patients?"

"But you're not convincing your patients, Herr Oberarzt," she protested. "You've got the wrong approach altogether."

I was not prepared to accept this kind of impertinence from a beginner, even if she was the daughter of the Regional Medical Officer. I sent her outside, and instructed her to wait for me in the ward office.

"There used to be doctors in this hospital once who had some human sympathy," Frau Brinkmann was lamenting. "You used to be one of them, Herr Oberarzt. But now there's a new spirit in this place, I suppose. Just remember that you're breaking up a family. I know—the family of a criminal. But then what else can I expect—the wife of a convict?"

I tried to console her, but she was crying uncontrollably. Besides, what consolation could I offer her? The truth about her husband was worse than she suspected. At that moment I envied Wolfgang Busch for the first time.

I had a serious row with Ellen Tschauner. Unless a person submitted to the hospital discipline like everybody else, I told her, he or she would have to go. At first she argued with me. Clearly she was not accustomed to being told off. But my violent anger seemed to have impressed her. Suddenly she laughed at me in a helpless sort of fashion, and promised to mend her ways.

14

MAY Day, the greatest holiday in our country's calendar, was casting its shadow forward. For Professor Brunke its first harbingers were not encouraging. He learned that his name was not on the list of Meritorious People's Doctors to be published on May Day. Neither his voluntary reconstruction shifts nor his Pavlov sleep-treatment ward had made the expected impression on his superiors. The Pavlov ward was suffering from a chronic lack of patients. It was at best half full, whereas all other wards in the hospital were continually short of beds. Not enough patients were suitable for sleep therapy, and of those chosen for it many refused. Much as Dr Pollak regretted this state of affairs, it looked very well in his statistics. Consumption of medicines in his ward was exceedingly small, thanks to the very small number of patients there, and the average time spent by patients in the ward was exceedingly short as anybody taken to the ward did his best to get away again in a hurry. Thus the impressive-looking statistics at least assured Pollak of finding himself among the 'leading workers.'

The commission charged with the task of choosing these 'leading workers' met a week before May Day and picked the names of those members of the hospital staff who were thought to deserve money prizes for their outstanding work during the past year. This system of money prizes had been invented by the Russian Communists when they discovered that the thesis that all men were equal and required the same reward for the same work tended merely to encourage the laziness innate in every human being. The money prizes distributed in East Germany every May Day, and, on 'Republic Day, October 8, are supposed to act as an incentive for good work and ambition. A proportion of the total wages bill paid by each undertaking to its workmen and office workers is kept back for these money prizes.

The ceremony at which the 'leading workers' were to be handed their prizes had been fixed by Paul Kranich for Friday, April 29, the last full working day before May Day. By means of the hospital grapevine, however, he had made sure that everybody due to receive a prize knew about it, and would therefore turn up. I too was informed that this year I was going to be honoured as a leading worker. Doctors are the only persons in our hospital who receive individual prizes. All other staff receive their prizes as collectives—that is, teams of three to six people normally working together.

During the lunch interval, just before two o'clock, the hospital staff assembled in the nurses' common-room. Paul Kranich had put on a clean shirt in honour of the occasion. He opened the ceremony with a little speech in which he announced that the international festival of all working people was again imminent. The hospital had every reason to be proud of its peaceful reconstruction work. Paul Kranich enjoyed the reputation of a great orator chiefly because he had a wonderful knack of stringing together the Party's slogans like beads on a thread. Short linking sentences were all he needed to pass from one slogan to another. The result was something like this: "This good piece of work is important, for: As We Work To-day, Thus We Shall Live To-morrow. Everybody must give a hand: Each One Of Us Must Do His Good Deed For Socialism. Always remember, colleagues: Man Stands at the Very Centre of Things. And not just the individual man: From the I to the We—that is our slogan. We improve our performance not in order to outshine others but to advance further together. It is this common work that matters, for: We Want To Become a Socialist Hospital."

After that he began to build up the suspense: "The best members of our hospital staff are now about to be presented with prizes. Well, now, who are these best people? We shall hear their names in a moment. I call upon our colleague, the Hospital Director, to perform the presentation of the prizes."

Professor Brunke stepped forward in a spotless snow-white coat and in white theatre trousers with an impeccable razor-edge crease. A clerk from the administration office handed him fifteen sealed envelopes bearing the names of those chosen for money prizes.

"I call upon the collective from the laundry," he intoned solemnly in a sonorous bass. While the audience applauded, the forewoman of the laundry stepped forward, received the envelope, and thanked the Professor with a handshake.

And so it went on. The collective from the X-ray department; the collective of Ward 3, where the first socialist brigade had been formed; the collective of the female staff of Casualty. Sister Anneliese, with the wart on a snub nose, and Frau Gummer stepped forward. Frau Gummer prided herself on being a regular recipient of money prizes. For years the secretarial staff had been envious of her, for they usually drew a blank while Frau Gummer, whom they regarded as a rival, enjoyed more powerful support among her colleagues on the trade-union committee. No one among those present suspected that this was to be Frau Gummer's last prize.

I found DM 425 in my envelope. That was an exceptionally large amount. The envelopes for the collectives as a rule contained only DM 150, which had then to be divided between the members of the team. This sharing out invariably caused bad blood, since the leading members of the teams, such as the ward Sisters, claimed a larger share than the trainees. In the end they usually settled for equal shares.

The ceremony was concluded by Paul Kranich intoning what used to be a West German musical hit—*Good-bye, Johnny*—but what in our country, played rather more slowly and sung to words by J. R. Becher, does service as our national anthem. "Resurrected from the ruins, marching forward arm in arm," we sang to the tune made popular many years ago by Hans Albers' film *Water for Canitoga.*

15

MAY 1, 1960, was a Sunday. Kukowa and I had agreed to be on call for the weekend. We started Saturday in Casualty. Frau Gummer met us with a bitter-sweet smile and red paper carnations. These she was selling on behalf of the trade-union committee, 50 pfennig apiece. "Pity red goes so badly with my complexion," Kukowa regretted, and put the carnation he had just bought on the window-sill. So that the little flower should not feel lonely, I tossed mine next to it. Then we began our surgery.

Frau Gummer had arranged for only a few patients to attend. In addition to those with appointments, however, a great many turned up unannounced. All of them were wearing red carnations in their buttonholes or on their blouses.

One of our first patients was a grey-haired building worker with a mole on his left cheek. On the card which Frau Gummer had made out for him the entry under 'condition complained of' consisted of the single word *Ulcus*. The Latin *ulcus*, without any further details, can mean a stomach ulcer or varicose ulcers of the legs. But as the man had come to Casualty I expected that it was his legs he was suffering from.

"Well, then, where's the pain?" I asked my routine question. The man looked at me in surprise. "No pain at all."

"In that case what have you come for?"

"Because elsewhere no doctor ever has any time. I ought to have my stomach examined."

"Do you suffer from stomach-ache?"

"No—yes—sometimes."

"But not at the moment?"

"No, not at the moment."

"Why then have you come to-day?"

"Well, you know, Herr Doktor—the pain can come back any time."

"When one eats pork sausage and washes it down with a lot of beer—is that it?"

The worker grinned.

"In that case you'd better go steady on the free beer to-morrow. And if on Monday you suffer from a stomach-ache I'll cut you open and have a good look."

"No, thank you," the man exclaimed, and disappeared.

We got a lot of his type in Casualty, wasting our time. Frequently we would get countrywomen who would nip in quickly, between their shopping and their next train home, to have themselves examined—just because it was free. Or we would get men coming in after a night's heavy drinking, begging for tablets. As an excuse they would sometimes show some slight scratch and say they were afraid of blood-poisoning. Under the rules no one could be turned away from Casualty. The public knew that, and therefore frequently came in with trifling complaints. Sometimes they merely wanted to reassure themselves that there was a doctor available for them if they needed one.

Later in the morning Paul Kranich waddled through Casualty on his crooked legs. An air of benign absent-mindedness hung about him, for this was one of the highlights of his political year. "You're marching with us to-morrow, colleague doctor?" he addressed me. "We rendezvous in the hospital courtyard at 0900 hours."

I regretted that I was on duty next morning, and Kukowa, unsolicited, associated himself with my regrets.

"You haven't got your red carnations yet?" Kranich asked severely.

Kukowa struck his chest with his fist. "If a man carries socialism in his heart, colleague Kranich, he always wears an invisible red carnation in his buttonhole."

Kranich decided not to have his festive mood marred by Kukowa's equivocal remarks. He moved on.

16

Fʀᴏᴍ Casualty we were in an excellent position to watch the departure of the hospital staff for their procession on Sunday morning. Frau Gummer was fussing about with a list, ticking off every one who had turned up. Of the two hundred members of the staff no more than eighty had arrived. A few of them were on duty, but a great many others simply shirked the procession. The nurses and Sisters were standing together in a small bunch, in their uniforms. Sister Eva had asked to be excused because of her condition. She was now six months pregnant, and would have found the rigours of the march-past too much for her. The male nurses and a few doctors had turned up in civilian clothes. Paul Kranich was scuttling about between the different groups, gesticulating and issuing directions. Now and again he would glance nervously at his wristwatch. He was waiting for male nurse Bollmann, who had been chosen for the privilege of carrying the hospital's flag.

At last Bollmann appeared in the driveway, walking bravely but not quite steadily. He was looking a little the worse for wear, and seemed to be making great speeches. He then asked for the hospital flag, a large red cloth banner with the emblem of the Free German Trade Union Federation, the State symbol of hammer and compasses, and the hospital's name, and with it took up position at the head of the marching column which had formed up meanwhile. The flagstaff was swaying a little, and forced the bearer to make compensating movements. There was no doubt that Bollmann had used the early hours of the morning to fortify himself for his honourable duties in some bar or other.

"A real activist can carry two flags in front of him as easily as one," Kukowa mocked. But for once he was mistaken. The moment the column got going Bollmann tripped, and was only just caught by Ernst Pfeifer. Paul Kranich cursed and called another male nurse from the medical department to the front of the column to carry the flag. Bollmann was looking pale and sick. He broke column and came reeling over towards us in Casualty. We laid him on an examination table and made him sip some of the coffee Kukowa had made for himself.

"I'm not the chap I was," Bollmann was groaning. "I've grown soft. In the old days, when I was with the parachutists, we used to booze all night and then do two days' and two nights' smart duty."

We had an uneventful morning. We knew, of course, that this was merely the lull before the storm, for long experience had taught us that the evening of May Day and the night invariably brought brisk business to Casualty. Mainly the result of brawls, or drunks falling down and hurting themselves.

I made use of my free time in the morning for a quick round of my patients. On my way to the wards I suddenly found myself facing an old friend: Frau Steinkopf, in a blue coat and a Sunday hat, fresh from visiting Granny Novotny. It was a surprise indeed. Our patient with the unquenchable optimism, the woman who had caused us so much anxiety. But now she was looking pale and worn, and her eyes were red from crying. When I asked her how she was she began to fish for her handkerchief.

I steered her into my office. "What's the trouble, Frau Steinkopf —pains again?" I asked.

She looked at me questioningly. "Tell me, Herr Oberarzt, is there such a thing as professional secrecy?"

"Certainly there is."

She was still hesitating. Tears were again welling up in her eyes. "I just don't know to whom I may speak openly. I'm so worried about my husband."

She told me, in great detail, that her husband, the master lock-smith, was being forced to join a production co-operative of members of his trade. At first they had merely tried to persuade him, but now they had resorted to threats and blackmail.

"You've met my husband, Herr Oberarzt," she continued. "You wouldn't recognize him now. He is heading straight for a nervous breakdown. He just can't stand up to the pressure much longer. He's lost nearly two stone."

"Won't he eat?"

"He has no appetite. But this isn't a case where a doctor can help. If he knew that he could remain boss in his own workshop he'd be well again by to-morrow. It's the worry."

An idea flashed through my mind. "And why shouldn't a doctor be able to help, Frau Steinkopf?" I asked. "Just give me a minute to think."

Quite a lot of craftsmen and artisans were still resisting absorption into production co-operatives. It certainly did not look as if the drive against independent craftsmen would end as successfully for the Party as had the forcible collectivization of the peasants. At the same time, the powers that be were anxious to preserve the outward appearance of voluntary entry. The strongest pressure was invariably applied to those whose resistance was expected to crumble soonest. Once a man had weathered the first onslaught of the storm he would usually be left alone.

Clearly what mattered in the Steinkopf case was to gain time. If the master locksmith could be snatched from the reach of the propagandists for a few days he would very probably be safe.

I suggested that Frau Steinkopf should come back with her husband in the afternoon and ask for me in Casualty. I told her I was fairly confident that I could help her husband.

"Nonsense, Herr Oberarzt," she said. "I just told you all about it because I happened to run into you, and because I needed someone to talk to. You looked after me while I was here, and I realized then that you were a person one could trust. That was all. There is nothing the matter with my husband."

I gave her one of those significant glances that are used in our country for conveying something one is afraid of putting into words. She understood, and promised to come.

17

In the afternoon the hospital personnel returned in close column. Those who had held out to the bitter end were treated in the hospital courtyard to hot sausages and free beer. This knowledge had acted as an incentive to many of them not to drift away from the procession prematurely. Frau Gummer, who came to see us in Casualty, was still dazed by "the stirring experience of belonging together," as she put it. On the way to the town centre there had been a good many hold-ups, as other enterprises tried to file into the procession. From all directions the working people had been converging on the city centre. The highlight of the occasion had been a march-past in front of a saluting base with Party officials, Army officers, and guests of honour. "We now welcome our colleagues from the State-owned enterprise Coal Retail," the loudspeakers would blare across the square. The marchers waved little flags or clapped their hands over their heads in the accepted 'friendship greeting.' Next, the colleagues from the hospital were welcomed. Behind the saluting base little rockets soared up into the air, spewing out small red flags, or black, red, and gold flags adorned with hammer and compasses. Most of all, however, Frau Gummer had been impressed by the radiologist of some other hospital. He had built a large mock-up of an X-ray apparatus on top of a motor-car and with it had demonstrated to the 'colleagues production workers' the constant loving solicitude shown by the medical profession for the people's health. Frau Gummer much regretted the fact that none of our doctors had conceived a similar idea.

"What a day!" she said rapturously. "A most impressive demonstration of those fighting for peace against the atom bomb policy of the West. A great victory for the cause of socialism."

"Yes, indeed," Kukowa said dreamily. "To fight peacefully—that's what gives us such a moral superiority over those unacquainted with this combination."

In the afternoon Frau Steinkopf came back with her husband. He really looked drawn and exhausted, his eyelids were twitching nervously, and he seemed very edgy. When a gust of wind slammed shut the door behind him he started violently. I took both of them to Frau Gummer's empty room and had a chat with them about their private worries. The following afternoon, the master locksmith told me, the decisive negotiations were to take place. He just did not know how he could pull his head out of the noose.

I had taken Kukowa into my confidence and examined Steinkopf together with him. The honest master locksmith was not quite sure what was going on, but he was instinctively prepared to escape into sickness, just like a schoolboy afraid of an examination on the following day. At first he wanted to tell us about his nervous troubles, about states of panic, and palpitations. But we did not encourage him along those lines, since what we needed was surgical symptoms.

Willingly he confirmed everything we wanted to know: rapid loss of weight, occasional sensations of fullness or pressure inside his stomach, weakness, discoloured stools. . . .

We soon had a long list of symptoms which looked useful. We told him he would have to come back the following morning for a thorough examination of his stomach. We would admit him to the surgical department for several days.

I took Frau Steinkopf aside and explained to her as openly as I dared: "Now don't be alarmed, there's no reason at all for anxiety —but just in case anybody asks, you tell them that your husband's been admitted to hospital on urgent suspicion of cancer of the stomach." I was saying a great deal more with my eyes than my lips, and she understood me all right.

18

WE WERE back to our normal daily routine. On Monday Paul Kranich wandered through the hospital, searching for faces he had missed in the procession. He was very ready with cheap sneers. Dr Pollak, for instance, was treated to the remark: "Too proud to march in the procession yesterday, eh? But not too proud to accept the money on Friday!"

There were quite a few people who had not marched in the procession. Matron Margot Kress, for instance, Sister Helga, Professor Zöllinger, the 'living corpse,' and even Dr Ellen Tschauner, the daughter of the Regional Medical Officer. Kukowa and I were treated by Kranich with the greatest respect, since we had an unimpeachable alibi. No doubt he had forgotten that we had not marched in the procession in past years either.

My women patients were still on very cool terms with me. Frau Brinkmann was taken away to the nursing centre on Monday. Normally it would take weeks or even months to have a patient collected for transfer. In March, however, a new centre for the chronically sick had been opened near our town, and there were still several vacancies there. Granny Novotny regarded me reproachfully whenever I passed her bed.

I now spent a great deal of time in the men's wards, which used to be under Reinfeld. The efforts of the socialist brigade, which was to support me there, were unfortunately evident only in the fact that medicines and dressings were used with excessive economy. Sister Anneliese was proud of the fact that the consumption of cottonwool had dropped by 20 per cent., and that of gauze by 15. The linoleum on the floor had become dull because Frau Piesewitz now made a tin of floor-polish go twice as far as before.

For Steinkopf, the master locksmith, we had got a bed ready in Ward 9. He was a good patient, and willingly submitted to all examinations. As expected, the tests were all negative. But the practical value of having admitted him became obvious on the very first afternoon. As soon as Frau Steinkopf informed the propaganda officials of the production co-operative that her husband had been admitted to hospital on suspicion of cancer they gave up their endeavours. They did not even fix a later date for negotiations. Presumably they told themselves that if Steinkopf had cancer he would have to close his workshop sooner or later anyway. So they left him to his fate.

Towards the end of his stay in hospital Steinkopf became friendly with his neighbour, a forty-five-year-old agronomist named Erich Neubauer. Neubauer, who was a member of an agricultural production co-operative, had had his appendix removed. Psychologically speaking, he was not the right company for Steinkopf.

During my morning round, while I was still at another patient's bed, I heard Neubauer say to Steinkopf: "Don't you worry, they'll get every one of you into a production co-operative in the end. Make no mistake—the fact that they've stopped pestering you now means nothing. I've seen it all in our village. Not one of the peasants has been allowed to keep his farm—not a single one of them."

I felt that I had better discharge Steinkopf. His neighbour was only filling his head with the very worries which we had tried to take off him. "Herr Steinkopf is to be discharged to-day," I decided after looking at the charts with the latest test results. "There is no suspicion any longer of any serious illness."

I turned to Neubauer. Three days had passed since his operation. "Moved your bowels yet?" I asked. This was a routine question on the third day after an operation. The answer was no.

I turned to Sister Anneliese and, as usual in such cases, ordered: "Enema with tepid saline solution."

When I returned to the ward on my afternoon round Steinkopf's bed was already occupied by a new patient. Next to it Neubauer was complaining about acute pain in his colon. He did not look like a man to fuss over slight discomfort. But normally there should be no pain after an enema. I was puzzled.

"Who gave him the enema?" I asked Sister Anneliese.

"Nursing auxiliary Pfeifer." I had Ernst Pfeifer called. He gazed at me with his meek cow's eyes, open-mouthed.

"Now then, Pfeifer," I said, "will you tell me what you did with this patient?"

He reflected for a moment. Then he remembered. "Salt enema."

"Did you use a tepid salt solution?"

"Yes."

"Where did you get the salt solution?"

"From the toilet," Pfeifer replied ingenuously.

Sister Anneliese and I exchanged glances. Saline solution in the lavatory?

"Yes, there's a bottle of it on the little shelf near the top," Pfeifer added.

I went out to the lavatory with him. I did not like the sound of this.

Pfeifer reached up and took down a bottle. On the label was a skull in heavy print. Underneath was the inscription: 'Spirits of salt.' The acid was used for cleaning the lavatory pan. The blood froze in my veins. "For heaven's sake, Pfeifer, is this what you used?"

He looked at me startled. "But I was told to. Sister Anneliese said so."

"What did Sister Anneliese say?"

"Salt . . . spirits of salt . . ."

"Salt solution."

"Yes, that's it."

"And you don't know the difference?"

He kept stammering: "Salt . . . salt . . ."

Fortunately, since he had not known how to warm the solution, he had diluted the concentrated hydrochloric acid with warm water from the tap.

I left Pfeifer where he was and called a male nurse from another ward. I instructed him to get an enema of sodium bicarbonate solution at once. I did not know what damage the hydrochloric acid had already done to the sensitive mucous membrane of the colon. Perhaps it was too late for counter-measures, but the bicarbonate of soda would at least neutralize any traces of acid. We just had to hope for the best.

Ernst Pfeifer had made several stupid mistakes before. Sister Anneliese had to supervise him constantly. Even when he was doing routine jobs of the kind that other auxiliaries learnt in next to no time he would again and again make mistakes. Now, for the first time, he had endangered a patient's life. That must not happen again.

I really felt sorry for Ernst Pfeifer. He was neither malicious nor recalcitrant—he merely lacked the amount of intelligence needed for the responsible job of a nurse. But we could not endanger our patients just to please him. Matron Margot Kress agreed with me. She reported the incident to the trade-union committee without whose consent a person could not be dismissed from his post. Thus ended the career of our socialist bridegroom and expectant father. Ernst Pfeifer took off his white jacket and once more put on his blue overalls. He finished up where he had started—with the outdoor staff.

For several days we were rather anxious about Erich Neubauer. The bicarbonate enema brought him only temporary relief. However, with a great deal of patience we eventually succeeded in overcoming the effects of his corroded tissues and in stimulating the body's own recuperative forces. Apart from several days of pain the mistake of our nursing auxiliary had no lasting consequences for the agronomist. He was discharged in normal health.

19

I GOT on quite well with Ellen Tschauner, our new houseman. Since I had made it clear that I would not tolerate any impertinence on her part, I was the only person she treated with respect. In her work she tried hard to give me as little cause for complaint as possible. She had even stopped wearing make-up on duty because she knew that I did not like it.

Towards everybody else, however, she continued to act the daughter of the Regional Medical Officer. She regarded Kukowa as a bigoted Party member. Hansen she despised because he was trying rather too crudely to ingratiate himself with her. His attempts at flirting with her merely irritated her: no doubt she realized that he was interested in the daughter only in order to get at the father. For the time being his connexions extended only as far as the District Medical Officer; the Regional Medical Officer was still beyond his reach.

I met her in the corridor one morning, smoking a cigarette, when she was supposed to be Hansen's second assistant. I asked her why she had not yet started scrubbing-up. "No, Herr Oberarzt," she replied, "I do not want to join Dr Hansen."

I was about to remind her very firmly of her duties when the chief came out of his office and asked me whether Kukowa could perform the first operation alone. He had to talk to me urgently. I had no hesitations about leaving the operation to Kukowa, but I was annoyed that I had to fulfil Ellen Tschauner's wish in this way. I had made up my mind to break her of her caprices. Now I had to take her away from Hansen and assign her to Kukowa. But there was nothing else I could do.

In Professor Zöllinger's office were two Russian officers and a short, plump woman. The chief told me that he had just done something he was not supposed to. He had promised Major Adrianov to operate on his wife. A glance at the Russian woman told me that it could only be a question of a goitre operation.

"I would like to ask you now to carry out the necessary examinations. Provided this is a non-toxic growth, and not a Basedow goitre, I am prepared to operate. Major Adrianov is not on good terms with the surgeon at the Soviet garrison hospital. For a number of reasons he would prefer to have his wife treated in a German hospital, even though this is against the rules. At the same time, if this turns out to be a toxic goitre I am not prepared to accept the responsibility."

I promised the chief to perform the examination carefully. The second officer turned out to be an interpreter, since Major Adrianov spoke but little German, and his wife no German at all. We got a private ward ready for Mme Adrianov on the first floor of the theatre block.

The chief had let himself in for a risky business. The Governments in Berlin and Moscow both insisted on a strict segregation of the Russian forces from the German civilian population. But Professor Zöllinger, a medical man of the old school, attached less importance to official regulations than to his Hippocratic oath, which obliges a physician to assist anyone who asks him.

Mme Adrianov was a quiet and co-operative patient. She watched us from her meek, slightly melancholy dark eyes as we examined her.

But these mute examinations were not really satisfactory. Although the young people nowadays are taught Russian at school, neither Sister Eva nor two probationer nurses were able to tell me what "Does this hurt?" was in Russian. Dr Pollak had lived in Russia for some time, but we were reluctant to consult him. We were afraid that he might diagnose the patient as ideally suited for his sleep therapy. Through sheer accident I discovered that Ellen Tschauner had quite a good knowledge of Russian. So she became our interpreter from then onward.

Our examinations turned out favourably. We repeated them several times, and were convinced that we were dealing with a non-toxic goitre which presented no dangers. Major Adrianov once more visited his wife at the hospital during the afternoon preceding the operation. As the chief was away, I talked to him. He was again accompanied by his interpreter. Major Adrianov was of medium height, with sparse hair and intelligent features. In contrast to the Russian officers I had met during the first few years after the War, he looked well-groomed and had good manners. The questions he asked all betrayed his anxiety for his Ninotchka. They had been happily married for twenty years, and he still loved her, although she had aged much more quickly than himself. She must have been a pretty and shapely young girl before she put on her matronly fat. Her melancholy dark eyes and her raven hair parted in the middle and drawn tightly to the back, where it was coiled into a chignon, still suggested her earlier good looks.

I did not take part in the operation. The chief took a younger colleague to assist him, so that the rest of our list should not suffer too much that day. Everything went according to plan. Professor Zöllinger was satisfied, and merely asked me to keep an eye on post-operative developments in the afternoon. He felt so confident that he drove off to his home, taking with him his books and papers for a few hours' undisturbed work. Before leaving the hospital he rang through to the Major's interpreter to tell him that the operation had been satisfactory.

In the afternoon, however, I was called away from my room by Sister Anneliese, who was looking after Mme Adrianov. The patient's pulse, she reported, had suddenly got very much faster. I broke off my round and at once went across to see her. Mme Adrianov had come round from the anaesthetic, but she was limp and apathetic. Her heart was racing. I counted 150 beats per minute. That was a bad sign. Such after-effects, whose cause is not yet fully understood, are not customary after ordinary goitre operations. It seemed, therefore, that, in spite of our negative tests, Mme Adrianov's had been a toxic goitre.

I rang up Professor Zöllinger at his home. He immediately returned to hospital.

Unfortunately, there is not much a doctor can do in the face of such complications. Medicines are no use when the heart and the circulation are upset by unknown causes. The patient sank into a deep coma. Professor Zöllinger diagnosed a typical Basedow coma, a dangerous condition occasionally encountered after an operation on a toxic goitre.

We tried desperately to save the patient's life. Professor Zöllinger's leathery face had turned ashen grey. He had hoped to avoid all public notice when he accepted the case against the regulations. And now this case was challenging him to a duel with death.

Towards the evening we realized that we were losing the struggle. Mme Adrianov was sinking more and more. The violent upheaval of her heart turned into agony. Shortly after nine her heart stopped.

Professor Zöllinger drove out to the Major that same evening, and himself broke the shattering news to him. Fate had been against us. For Professor Zöllinger the sad incident fortunately remained without consequences. Neither from the Russian nor from the German authorities were recriminations made against him. Adrianov merely squeezed the chief's hand in silence. Even in his grief he did not allow himself to give way to suspicions.

Part Four

1

Every Tuesday and Friday Professor Zöllinger did a 'chief's round' at four in the afternoon. All the medical staff of the hospital who were available at that time would await him in the duty office of the first group of wards. One Friday about the middle of May the chief arrived earlier than usual. I was still alone in the office, sitting at the desk. Professor Zöllinger was clearly glad of the chance of a private conversation. He offered me one of the cigarettes which he invariably carried, although he did not smoke himself. "There's something important I've got to discuss with you," he said.

He hoisted himself on to the edge of the desk, ignoring the chair I had offered him. "From next Monday you'll have to take on the acting job of a *Chefarzt*," he continued. "You probably know the hospital in the district town, some twelve miles from here."

"I have heard Matron Kress speak of it," I replied. "I believe she spent some time there."

"That's the one. The *Chefarzt* of the surgical department there is one Dr Lummelsheim. He was appointed to his post against my advice three years ago. Do you know anything about him?"

I knew him by name only.

"I'd be glad if you could drive over to-morrow morning, have a look round, and give me your impressions at lunch-time."

I had a feeling that this was going to be a delicate task.

On Saturday morning, towards nine o'clock, I pulled up outside the hospital. While I was still at the wheel, gazing at the brick façade of the building—dating back to the thirties—three gentlemen emerged. All three of them seemed to be arguing excitedly. The one in the middle, a tall, lean man, suddenly turned about and made as if to go back inside. The other two, who were much shorter, gripped his wrists and motioned to a car that was standing a short distance in front of mine. Reluctantly, and still arguing furiously, the lean man allowed himself to be led towards it. Then suddenly he again started gesticulating, and tried to turn back. His two companions became more determined and virtually dragged him into their car. One of these companions I recognized as our District Medical Officer, Dr Schwiers. This was the first time I had seen him without the chewed end of a cigar between his teeth. He and the tall, lean man got into the back, and the third man got in next to the driver. The third man, as I was to learn later, was the local District Medical Officer; he had merely asked his colleague Dr Schwiers from our town to come over to support him.

I asked the porter the meaning of the scene I had witnessed. The porter was furious. "That was our *Chefarzt* from the surgical department," he explained. "The two District Medical Officers intercepted him here and prevented him from entering the hospital. It's disgraceful. Trying to tell the chief he's sick. Lot of nonsense. Hope he comes back soon. And what do *you* want?"

"I'm deputizing for him," I said curtly.

A probationer nurse conducted me to the administrative office, where I saw a man with a large, flat face and grey hair cut *en brosse*. His age, at a guess, was between fifty-five and sixty. "Padereit," he introduced himself. He was the most powerful man in the hospital, for he held all the key positions. He was at the same time the administrator, the head of the hospital Party organization, and chairman of the hospital trade-union committee.

"You're taking on a difficult legacy, Herr Doktor," he welcomed me in a broad East Prussian accent. "Dr Lummelsheim was a good boss. If only he didn't have that addiction! Time and again he'd solemnly promise the District Medical Officer to give it up. But he just couldn't. Well, you'll have to try to inspire as much confidence as Dr Lummelsheim, in both the staff and the patients!"

Presently I went round to introduce myself to the chief of the Medical Department, a Dr von Sorbeck. He looked just like a caricature of an old Prussian army doctor, and he spoke with a rasping voice in short, clipped sentences. I did not think this type of doctor still existed. Von Sorbeck must have been the last surviving representative of this unlovable breed. Apart from Lummelsheim, he was the only fully trained doctor in the entire hospital.

Padereit, the administrator, and Dr von Sorbeck called a staff meeting for the late morning, at which they announced that the chief of the Surgical Department had gone on sick leave for the time being. I was then introduced as his deputy. On all sides I met with suspicious and curious glances. My medical collaborators in the Surgical Department were four young housemen. Not one of them could operate independently. They were known in the hospital as the quartet. From the very start they left me in no doubt that they disapproved of my appointment. The only face I knew was that of a man called Scholz, a male theatre nurse. I had often seen him at our hospital off duty, when he visited Matron Kress. During the past few weeks—in fact, ever since Pütz of Cologne had vanished—she had been warming up an old love affair. The two knew each other from the days when our Matron was at the District Hospital.

At lunch-time I reported back to Professor Zöllinger. "From what I have heard, Dr Lummelsheim appears to be a morphine addict," I said.

My chief confirmed this. "But very popular in the hospital," he pointed out. "You're going to have a difficult time in every respect."

I was not looking forward to next Monday.

Early on Monday morning I summoned the quartet to my office. I offered a cigarette to each of them in turn, but they all declined.

"Very well, gentlemen," I said, trying not to seem offended. "What operations had Dr Lummelsheim planned for to-day?"

One of the four replied: "A reopening of an abdomen because of after-effects of a gall-bladder operation."

I thought I had misheard. "A reopening?"

The spokesman for the four, a fair, freckled young man, nodded. "Yes, of course. Some complications have cropped up."

I was beginning to be intrigued. "But surely that will only be adhesions?"

"Possibly," the freckled man replied. "In that case we'll separate them again."

I wondered what on earth Lummelsheim could have taught the young men.

"Have any of you worked at any other hospital before this?" I asked.

They shook their heads.

"Well, then, let's go and do our round," I decided.

I asked first of all to be taken to the woman patient who was complaining of pains after her gall-bladder operation.

"Can I see the X-rays?" I asked the theatre Sister.

"X-rays? No X-rays were taken."

The patient was scrutinizing me severely. "Is that the doctor who is to operate on me?" she asked the Sister in a whisper. Then she protested angrily: "I want to be operated on by Dr Lummelsheim. Where is Dr Lummelsheim?"

"He's ill," I said casually, and continued talking to the theatre Sister.

"Then I'll wait till he's well again," the patient lamented.

The housemen exchanged satisfied glances.

Pains occurring some time after a gall-bladder operation are as a rule due to adhesions. In such cases there is no point whatever in operating a second time, for the adhesions invariably recur.

"I don't want to be operated on by you," the patient protested.

I smiled at her. "Why, that's splendid. As it happens, I've no intention of operating on you. The operation is cancelled," I announced to the Sisters and nurses. I carefully ignored their startled expressions and incipient muttering. Accompanied by the housemen, I proceeded on my round. What I saw in the wards was terrifying. It was the legacy of a man who, once a skilled surgeon, was now a physical and mental wreck. Towards the end Dr Lummelsheim had no longer been able to operate correctly. What was even worse, he had been unable to diagnose and assess his own condition. As long ago as three years, when he assumed his post, the authorities had been warned. Professor Zöllinger and other specialists had pointed out the danger. But the Party had shielded the good Party member. True, Lummelsheim had been cautioned because of some proven offences by him against the Drug Act. But apart from that nothing happened. Nobody could tell what damage he had done over the three years. All I saw was the most recent results of his work.

Several patients had festering wounds. It does, of course, happen now and again that a wound goes septic after an operation. But if this happens on any appreciable scale it suggests that the surgical work is not being done in adequately aseptic conditions. Other patients had incision hernias. When operations have to be repeated, and wounds reopened, there is always a risk that the scars may lack sufficient resistance to the pressure of the underlying tissue. Abdominal scars in particular are apt to give in those conditions, and through this hernia a part of the peritoneum and the intestines may be forced out. This was the kind of thing that might easily have happened to the woman on whom we were due to operate again that morning.

Finally I found myself by the bed of a young man who looked pale and tired. He was a twenty-seven-year-old worker, a man of good stature and powerful physique. "A very tragic case," one of the housemen whispered into my ear. "Dr Lummelsheim has given him up. Persistent haemorrhages."

The patient's advanced degree of anaemia was obvious at a glance. A test showed that he had only a quarter of the haemo-globin that is found in a healthy person. The man was slowly bleeding to death, and was bound to die of progressive debility during the next few days.

I ordered the patient to be taken to an examination room. There I established that he was losing bright red blood from his colon. The brighter the blood, the nearer must be the source of the bleeding to the anus. Clearly Dr Lummelsheim had concluded, after a cursory look at the patient, that he was losing blood from some point well inside the abdominal cavity. Presumably he put it down as an inoperable malignant tumour. With the lack of judgment typical of the drug addict, he had failed to carry out any further examination following his spot diagnosis. It took me only a few minutes to find the cause of the trouble. The young man was suffering from a bleeding haemorrhoid. We had to operate at once, to avoid further loss of blood. Subsequently we transfused him with blood from the blood bank. The vigorous young man whom Dr Lummelsheim had abandoned to his fate recovered within a few days.

2

WHEN I had finished my operation I found Padereit waiting for me in my office. "I thought you might find it helpful to your work here to know a little about the background of the animosities in our hospital."

"What animosities?" I asked.

"As you know, Dr Lummelsheim was picked up the day before yesterday and taken off to be cured of his addiction. But that is only a temporary end to a quarrel which has been going on for two years. It began when Dr von Sorbeck took over the Medical Department. The two chiefs did not get on with each other from the word go. I don't know if it was just a matter of personalities. You've met Dr von Sorbeck. He comes from an old officers' family. His father was an army surgeon. He was brought up in that tradition. There's no doubt he is not a pleasant person, or an easy one to get on with. He expects a lot of his fellow workers, but he also expects a lot of himself. *Chefarzt* Dr Lummelsheim, on the contrary, was an entirely different type. He was easy-going to the point of indifference. He had a disarming way of handling people, and had a cheerful and happy disposition. Now and then he might be absent-minded and grumpy, and then one would try to keep out of his way. Undoubtedly he was once an extremely skilful surgeon. And he knew how to keep this reputation alive. Everybody looked upon him as a first-class surgeon."

"I've no doubt that he was brilliant once," I interposed.

Padereit continued: "When he joined us three years ago he already was a very sick man. True, he still managed to pull of most operations. But now and again he would make mistake which surprised the rest of our doctors. But at least they could keep him out of the theatre when he was too much under the in fluence of his drug. His cheerful nature helped them in this. Besides he then had an *Oberarzt* who could stand in for him. All tha changed when Dr von Sorbeck joined us. He introduced stric discipline in the Medical Department. He would not tolerat unpunctuality, carelessness, or muddle. His derogatory remark about the lax state of affairs in the Surgical Department were o course reported to Dr Lummelsheim. Now Dr Lummelsheim wa also the Hospital Director, and hence von Sorbeck's superior. N doubt he regarded von Sorbeck, a younger and more energeti man than himself, as a potential rival. Good-natured though h normally was, Dr Lummelsheim would instantly bristle when vo Sorbeck's name was mentioned. He thought up all kinds o moves to make von Sorbeck's life difficult. And in this campaig he enjoyed the support of the staff of both departments."

"You mean Dr von Sorbeck was increasingly driven into isola tion?"

"He's always been a lonely man. He hasn't many friends in th hospital. Naturally, he resisted vigorously. He noticed Dr Lummels heim's slip-ups and taxed him with them. In the end he tried t make him promise not to operate any more. But in this he wa unsuccessful. He next went to the District Medical Officer, and t various authorities and Party bodies, and informed them that D Lummelsheim was a morphine addict and a public danger."

"And that didn't do any good either?"

"Dr Lummelsheim immediately counter-attacked. He went t the same authorities and denounced Dr von Sorbeck as a re actionary and a politically unreliable person. Things came to suc a pass that the District Medical Officer found himself compelle to come down in favour of one rival or the other. As you ar aware, he decided eventually, for medical reasons, to drop h friend Dr Lummelsheim."

Padereit left me. I now knew the background of my appointment, but I still failed to understand why so many of the hospital staff were treating me in a hostile manner. At last I asked my old friend, the male theatre nurse Scholz.

Scholz knew the answer. "Most of them believe it was you who administered the final push which led to Dr Lummelsheim being taken to an institution for treatment, Herr Doktor. Everybody's so used to intrigues here they think that you must have conspired with Dr von Sorbeck to squeeze out Dr Lummelsheim in order to become *Chefarzt* yourself. Dr Lummelsheim was popular because he made no rules, because no one was made to work very hard under him, because there were no strict duty rotas, and because..."

"Because?"

"Because he had a few accomplices among the staff who were covering up for him. Most of the younger people had no idea what was going on. But we old hands knew all about it. If you find some case-histories incomplete, believe me there are reasons for it. Then there were some people on the staff who made sure that Dr Lummelsheim always got fresh supplies of morphine. You've got to know these things, Herr Doktor, if you want to get anywhere."

My endeavours to forestall further intrigues were jeopardized by two administrative officials sent to the hospital by the local District Medical Officer. They were instructed to find out whether Dr Lummelsheim had ever obtained morphine by illegal means. In the course of these investigations suspicion fell on Sister Martha, one of the oldest and most experienced Sisters in the hospital, of having known about Dr Lummelsheim's practices.

Sister Martha, a short, stocky woman with the rosy cheeks of a peasant, had been in charge of the poison book. This poison book now became the hub of all investigations by the two officials. Having spent all morning examining the various entries, they summoned Sister Martha during the lunch-break. I was asked to be present at the questioning.

We sat down in my office—the administrative officials Klee and Brasch, Sister Martha, and myself. Klee was the spokesman.

"A large amount of morphine appears to have been used in this hospital, Sister Martha," he began.

"That's not my responsibility," she replied coolly.

He pointed to the names of patients who had undergone perfectly simple operations and had subsequently, according to the entries in the book, been given morphine.

"Herr Dr Lummelsheim did not want his patients to suffer unnecessary pain," she said.

Now Brasch intervened. "I've got the names of two patients here who have not yet been discharged. Would you like me to question them?"

"Question them about what?"

"Whether they've really been given morphine."

Sister Martha looked at him in confusion and was silent.

"All right," he said. "Let's go to the ward."

Sister Martha was staring at the entries. "Perhaps I made a mistake," she stammered.

"You most certainly did," Brasch said harshly. "What's more, I know who got the ampoules. You merely entered the names of patients in the book in order to cover up for Dr Lummelsheim. Am I right?"

She shook her head resolutely. "I gave the ampoules to Herr Dr Lummelsheim, because he wished to give the morphine injections himself. Whether he did so or not I can't tell. But I have acted correctly throughout, and not falsified any entries."

Klee was leaning over towards her. "You knew very well, Sister Martha, how much the *Chefarzt* depended on the drug. You helped him to get hold of morphine. Why?"

She could not stand up to his searching scrutiny. She hid her face in her hands and began to sob.

"I'm asking you why, Sister Martha."

When she continued to be silent he went on: "You made yourself an accomplice in the sufferings of the many patients on whom Dr Lummelsheim operated. You knew perfectly well that he was making more and more mistakes, as the drug undermined his personality. And yet you kept him supplied with new ampoules. Why?"

"Out of pity," she sobbed. "Herr Dr Lummelsheim could no longer live without the drug."

"And you had no pity for the patients, for all the poor people who had entrusted themselves to him? You made yourself criminally culpable out of pity?"

"I did not falsify anything," she exclaimed. "Oh, what's the use —you don't understand."

Klee dismissed Sister Martha. He wanted to hear my opinion as a doctor. "You must remember," I said when Sister Martha had gone, "that the Sister was under pressure from her chief. What should she have done? Say no and denounce him? The fact that Dr Lummelsheim was a morphine addict has been known to all the authorities for years. But he was allowed to continue in his office. That's a fact Sister could not have changed, even if she had made a full report to the authorities."

Klee interrupted me. "But it is clear that she was a party to the false entries."

"It's by no means clear," I contradicted. "It is quite customary for a chief or any other doctor to draw morphine to give to a patient himself. There's no rule that the Sister in charge of the drug-book must be present during the injection, or make sure that the patient is in fact given the drug."

Klee and Brasch exchanged glances. "Very well," Klee said. "We shall include your remarks in our report for the District Medical Officer. I don't suppose any charge will be made against Sister Martha."

He called Sister Martha back and told her she had me to thank for being kept out of all further inquiries.

3

SEVERAL of Dr Lummelsheim's victims still in our wards were beyond my help. The incision hernias of two corpulent women, for instance, were not operable. In future they would have to wear trusses. With a fat person, even if the hernia is pushed back through the operation scar, there is always the danger that the scar tissue will yield once again.

A few other hernias, however, we dealt with during the next few days. For the first operation of this kind I chose two of the quartet to assist me—the fair houseman with the freckles and a stocky young man with a Berlin accent.

I had been washing my hands for five minutes when the two at last turned up in the theatre. They were genuinely surprised to find me there already. I used the period of our scrubbing-up to ask them about their personal circumstances. The freckled young man, by name Dieter Thorn, was a local. He had studied in Leipzig and Jena, and then come back to his native town to take up a post as houseman. The short, stocky man was from Berlin, and had also studied there. Two years ago his father, a railwayman, had been transferred to the vicinity of the district town. Since housemen were in desperately short supply in the smaller towns, the son had been made to take up a post there.

The two had spent barely five minutes scrubbing their hands and forearms when they wanted to dip them in the alcohol solution. Evidently this kind of surgical lick-and-promise had been customary under Dr Lummelsheim. No wonder so many wounds had gone septic.

Our patient that day was a woman of fifty with an incision hernia after two gall-bladder operations. I had decided to operate on her, although she was rather obese and I was by no means certain that my operation would be successful.

I made an incision through the skin, exposed the hernia, and slit the peritoneum and turned it back. Under the pressure from inside the peritoneum had bulged out like a balloon. After slitting open the bulge and forcing back the contents, I resected the part of the peritoneum which had formed the sac, and then sewed up the remaining edges.

I did not think the abdominal wall would stand up to this operation. Sutures of catgut and silk are apt to cut through skin tissue that has a poor blood supply through repeated stitching. I therefore decided to try a skin graft. This entailed a second, though minor, operation on the patient's thigh. From the skin there I cut an oblong patch, and with it I closed the abdominal wound, sewing it up crossways, in the way a boot is laced up.

I could feel how I rose in the estimation of the two housemen. They had never seen a hernia repaired in this way. Dr Lummelsheim had as a rule discharged his patients with a truss, and made no attempt to correct his earlier mistakes. Perhaps the young doctors were beginning to suspect that there was more to surgery than they had learned so far from their sick chief.

For the time being, however, I still found it difficult to overcome their passive resistance. They had grown accustomed to an easy life, and had not yet come to realize the seriousness of the profession they had chosen. The very first days convinced me that it had not been customary at this hospital to observe hours of duty. Dr Lummelsheim had been indifferent to discipline. He himself had put in only a few hours a day at the hospital, and had been unconcerned by the fact that everybody else came and went as they pleased. This kind of slackness—for which the patients had to pay in the end—had to be stopped.

To my annoyance I also discovered that the young housemen had never been taught to write proper case-histories. Nearly all records were too short and full of gaps. Important information about the background of patients' complaints and about past treatment was totally absent.

I spent every lunch-hour going over the case-histories. I summoned the young housemen, sometimes individually and sometimes in twos, and put them through a regular class. Patiently and persistently, I made them see what information a case-history must contain in order to preclude fatal errors in treatment. In between I dictated several case-histories myself, to serve as specimens.

4

I HAD instructed Sister Martha to keep me supplied with black coffee whenever midday drowsiness came over me. "You can't go on like that, Herr Chefarzt," she said to me on the third day. "No one can work at that pace. You should go out and get some fresh air for at least half an hour. We've got quite a nice public park near the hospital. I bet you haven't been there yet." Ever since I had saved her from prosecution in connexion with the morphine affair, Sister Martha looked after me like a mother.

She was probably quite right. I had taken on rather a lot for the first few days. The neglect of three years could not be put right in three days. I hung my white coat on the hook, slipped on my jacket, and walked out.

The summer heat hit me as I stepped out into the courtyard. The sky above was clear and blue. The nearest way to the public park was across the courtyard and along a cinder-covered passageway used by lorries and horse-drawn carts delivering supplies to the hospital. The air tasted of dry dust. Iridescent flies buzzed around me as I reached the corner of the yard. They were swarming about the refuse bins. Casually I lifted the lid of one of the bins. It was filled to the brim with sausage and cheese sandwiches. Whole swarms of flies rose up. There was a stench of rancid fat and mouldering cheese. I dropped the lid in alarm. Memories of the hungry years rose up before me, when every slice of bread had been a precious gift. I turned on the spot and went to see Padereit to complain about this senseless waste.

"Ah, Herr Doktor," he said, with a cunning smile on his broad, flat face. "We are not responsible for the smell."

"It's not just the smell," I replied. "There are also swarms of flies there. Refuse bins like that near a hospital are a source of infection."

Padereit was still smiling, but this time about my naïveté. We sat down on a garden seat, for I had caught him painting his fence.

Speaking slowly and savouring every word, he now delivered to me a lecture on planned economy.

In the past, he informed me, the hospital refuse had gone to fatten five to seven pigs annually. An old-age pensioner who lived near by and had nothing else to do had enjoyed feeding the refuse to the pigs. In the autumn and winter the pigs had been slaughtered. Presently, however, a directive had come from above that the fattening of pigs at the hospital must cease. All refuse had to go to the State-owned pig-fattening enterprise.

Although the State-owned pig-fattening enterprise had a considerable sty with a great many pigs, they lacked workers for collecting refuse from outside. Even if the pig-fattening personnel occasionally had a few minutes to spare out of their eight-hour day, they had neither lorries nor horse-drawn transport for collecting the refuse bins from the hospital. Thus the pigs of the State-owned fattening enterprise were on short rations, while at the same time their allotted feed was mouldering and rotting in our refuse bins.

"Yes, Herr Doktor," Padereit added. "That's what is called planning."

I was astonished at the Party man's frank remarks. Padereit had once been an official in a senior Party office in Berlin. His appointment as administrator of a small hospital had clearly been a step down. He presently referred to it himself. "There are a lot of wrong people in the planning bureaux," he said. "I was there myself once, but I realized that I'm a simple man and didn't belong there. Oh, yes, I've carried a Party card for a very long time and could be right at the top to-day. But, you know, I really feel happier here. A hospital is just small enough to keep an eye on the whole thing, and when I get a bit bored at my desk I pick up my tools and do what repairs are needed. I started out as a worker, and I still like being one. Unfortunately, many of us have forgotten our origins." He was sensible enough to realize his limitations. For the hospital, however, it would have been better still if he had remained with his tools permanently. A moment later I had another illustration of the kind of planning conducted by minor officials.

"Surely," I suggested, "it should be possible to cut only as many sandwiches as are actually eaten by the patients?"

He shook his bristly grey head.

"But the ward Sister does not know how much the patients want to eat."

"Can't she ask them?"

"That would mean additional work for her."

"True enough, but the cutting of sandwiches which aren't afterwards eaten means a great deal of additional work."

"I don't deny that. But we've got plenty of labour for cutting sandwiches. Asking the patients how many they propose to eat, on the other hand, means a special journey for the Sisters—a journey which at present they don't have to make."

I could not help smiling. But Padereit was perfectly serious. His was the typical logic of the small-time organizer. Any work envisaged in the plan was sacrosanct. Anything not in the plan was beyond discussion.

"It's not a bad idea at that," he conceded—chiefly, I thought, out of politeness. "Why don't you try to introduce your new system, Herr Doktor?" In spite of the fine weather and my good intentions, I immediately returned to my department and summoned the ward Sisters to me. When I told them about my observations and outlined my suggestions I could see reluctant faces all round me. Impossible! Out of the question—as if they were not overburdened enough with work! I estimated that each of the Sisters would need no more than five minutes for this extra round.

Moreover, I ought to explain that there was no shortage on paper of Sisters, nurses, or doctors at this hospital. All the posts on the establishment were filled. What there was an acute shortage of was trained personnel. The good nurses and Sisters had all drifted to bigger hospitals or to West Germany. The gaps had been filled with auxiliary labour.

After the plan had been given a rather cool reception by everybody else, Sister Martha, when her turn came to speak, nodded eagerly. "Yes, of course, Herr Chefarzt," she said. "We'll do that in future without any difficulty. I'll see to it that the kitchen is notified well in advance in future."

Thus the new system was introduced. As was to be expected, it worked perfectly well.

5

THE morning round had become the best part of my day. It was then that I saw the fruits of my work. The twenty-seven-year-old worker whom Dr Lummelsheim had condemned to bleeding to death after a cursory diagnosis was recovering splendidly. He had an excellent appetite, and was gaining in strength from day to day. In a few days' time we could discharge him. The woman whose hernia we had closed with a skin graft from her thigh was likewise in good shape. I was confident that the grafted patch of skin would take. Dieter Thorn, the freckled houseman, was proud to have assisted me during that—to him—strange operation. His opposition gradually gave way to admiration. Moreover, he was visibly enjoying learning new things from me, and I noticed that his enthusiasm was beginning to infect the rest of the quartet. In the past the four housemen had displayed a tepid attitude to their work, and had tried to dodge it whenever possible. They had not yet discovered the happiness and satisfaction which our profession holds for those who dedicate themselves to it whole-heartedly.

From then onward I got on well with the quartet. The patients, too, were beginning to show more confidence in me. The news that the young worker with the apparently persistent haemorrhage had been cured soon spread throughout the ward. There was also much appreciative gossip about the operation on the hernia. Naturally, both achievements were no more than could be reasonably expected of any competent surgeon, but by comparison with Dr Lummelsheim I was bound to appear a genius.

The only trouble I had was with the local chemist. At the beginning of my second week at the hospital Padereit, the administrator, informed me bluntly that my consumption of medicines was too high. Admittedly I had prescribed a lot of expensive antibiotics to treat the festering operation wounds. But Padereit was not interested in medical explanations, which he could not understand anyway. Silently he spread out the chemist's bills before me, and it was clear enough that mine were about twice as big as Dr Lummelsheim's. I took a closer look at the individual items, and discovered to my amazement that the chemist had charged all medicines at the retail price, although hospitals were of course entitled to a reduction.

During my lunch-hour I went to see the local chemist and questioned his bills. He regretfully shrugged his shoulders. "The sums I charged you are quite correct; we are not allowed to make any reductions for hospitals."

"Surely," I objected, "the money does not come out of your pocket?" His shop, like all other chemist's shops in our country, belonged to the State. The chemist merely received a salary for running it. "I, on the other hand, am not allowed to exceed the hospital's budget. Now, the hospital in the regional town, where I used to work as an *Oberarzt*, has its own dispensary. In future I shall try to get all my medicines from there."

The chemist turned bright purple with fury. "I shall lodge the strongest possible complaint," he shouted. "It's against all the regulations. It is the task of my shop to supply the local hospital. The prices are prescribed and I can't alter them."

I had to smile at his zeal. "If you were the proprietor of this shop I would understand your excitement. As it is I would merely be relieving you of a lot of work and, for the same sum, I would be getting a great many more medicines. Neither you nor I would be losing under such an arrangement, and my patients would derive considerable advantage from it."

"I've got a target to fulfil, Herr Doktor," he moaned. "I don't get a commission on my turnover, but my salary scale depends on my turnover all the same." I had no wish to harm the chemist. After all, why should I care whether the hospital's money was going to one State account or another? In any case, I shall not stay at this hospital very long. Professor Zöllinger, on whom I called from time to time, was making it quite clear that he would ask for me back very shortly. The moment a new *Chefarzt* had been found I should return to my old job.

This meant that at most I had another five weeks. My annual leave was due to begin early in July, and in our country you cannot change the date of a holiday. You either stick to the fixed date or else do without a holiday altogether.

6

TOWARDS the end of May we were finally able to move into our new flat. Busch's last pieces of furniture had meanwhile found purchasers among the factory staff. At long last we had a home of our own, a place to put our feet up. Ruth was happy, Angelica had a room of her own, and I no longer had to spend my evenings in that depressing attic. Now every evening I looked forward to going home. I was on the telephone, and if necessary could be summoned to the hospital even during the night. The twelve miles or so from our flat to the district hospital in the small provincial town I covered in next to no time by car every morning and evening. Naturally, my petrol vouchers for nine gallons a month did not run to this luxury, but Padereit saw to it that my tank was filled up at the hospital's official pump, free of charge, whenever necessary.

Every evening I would stride proudly through all the rooms of our new flat. No medieval lord of the manor could have been happier or more secure in his tenure. True, for the moment we had very few pieces of furniture, but that only made the rooms seem larger and more spacious.

After supper Ruth and I were reclining in the sitting-room, in easy chairs, smoking cigarettes. "What's it feel like?" I asked her.

She let her head drop back ecstatically. "Heavenly."

"Would you still want to go to the West?"

She gazed at me with her large, expressive eyes. "But of course. Wherever you go I go. But if you are staying here I stay here. Aren't you ever going to understand that a flat to me comes only second in importance? I would even move back into an attic if we had to—if need be for years."

I leapt to my feet, surprised. I had firmly believed that Ruth would change her views once she had a flat of her own.

"I'm delighted to hear it," I said. "I underrated you, Ruth. To be perfectly honest, I thought you were one of those wives who are always looking for a better nest. Now you've got one, and you're prepared to give it up again."

"I don't know why you should be so surprised."

"Perhaps I ought to have tried you harder," I said. "A pity I'm such a bad actor, else I would have played a little scene and faced you with a serious decision."

"You ought to have tried it," she chuckled. "I should have gone with you all the same. But what would you do if I told you I wanted to leave now? Say to-morrow morning, by the first train to Berlin? Now, don't lie to me. Tell me quite frankly what you would do."

I considered. "To-morrow morning is out, Ruth. I'm the only man on the district hospital staff who can operate. What's to become of the seventy patients in the surgical department? To-morrow morning I've got to operate on an old man. He'll die within the week unless I help him. If I leave, my patients will, so to speak, be orphaned. You can see for yourself, Ruth—these are weighty arguments."

She kissed me, laughing. "Never mind the arguments! You don't have to justify yourself so furiously, Peterkin. I leave the decision entirely to you."

7

IN VAIN was a successor sought for Dr Lummelsheim. Such few applicants as came forward lacked either the political or the medical qualifications required for the post. As for myself, I was not even in the running for a *Chefarzt* post because I carried no Party card.

Another *Oberarzt* was a loyal comrade, but had twice failed his specialist's examination. The well-paid and much-coveted *Chefarzt* vacancy just could not be filled.

The date of my leave was drawing near. "You're going on leave," Professor Zöllinger decided, when I told him my worries. "And if the District Medical Officer has not found a successor for Dr Lummelsheim by the end of June I'm going to call you back to our hospital. I'm going on leave in August myself, and shall need you to stand in for me. If a man's on duty for ten or twelve hours a day, and moreover does night duty at least twice a week, he's got to relax some time. Doctors with nervous breakdowns are no use to anybody."

Not till I had taken up my temporary post in the little country town did I realize the acuteness of the shortage of doctors in our country. In this little town, of nearly 10,000 inhabitants, there was only one general practitioner left. He was on the go from early morning until late at night. His waiting-room was not big enough to hold the patients for morning surgery. They would overflow into the hall and on to the stairs, and, even if it were raining, out into the street.

I had no idea what was to become of the surgical department when Professor Zöllinger called me back. But the District Medical Officer eventually hit on a solution. The hospital would in future accept only post-operative cases. Operations would no longer be performed there. Patients needing operations were taken by ambulance to Professor Zöllinger's hospital. In a few cases this drive to the regional centre was a race against death.

No doctor who has seen the disastrous consequences of the shortage of doctors in our country would go to the West irresponsibly, or merely for the sake of a better life. Certainly all the fugitive doctors of my acquaintance who had taken this course had left not for material reasons but because they were escaping from the State Security Service, like Gerd Reger, or avoiding forcible service, like Horst Reinfeld, or because of conflicts of conscience, like Wolfgang Busch. All three of these had meanwhile written to us.

Reger's letters ran to many pages, since his practice in Eastern

Bavaria left him much free time. This practice, he was complaining, had proved anything but a secure livelihood. In that poorest district of the Federal Republic the doctors too remained poor. Several of his colleagues from neighbouring villages had already drifted to the big towns. Certainly Gerd Reger did not lead in his new home the kind of carefree life we had pictured at first.

Reinfeld and Ute Weltz had been taken on at a small hospital near Frankfurt. He as a junior doctor, she as a Sister. They had to live carefully, but they could manage.

Wolfgang Busch, the idealist who had given up a certain career and a fine flat, had found a junior post in a hospital in the Ruhr. He was having difficulties about getting his specialist's status recognized, since the examination in our country is not valid in West Germany. True, no specialist's examination is required in the Federal Republic, but it takes a good deal of time and frequently annoyance before a man is recognized as a specialist. Busch had received a resettlement grant, and had furnished a modest small flat, but he was a little worried whether he would be able to find the rent regularly. For the time being he had no prospects of promotion, whereas if he had stayed he would soon have been an *Oberarzt*. Even so, he was saying in his letters, he was happy in his new home because he could work without constant psychological stress.

Shortly before my leave a letter was passed on to me at the district hospital from Lola. Sister Eva had forwarded it.

Lola Ried! Time had caused her image to fade. The colours had been washed out of it. Lola reminded me of a period when I had been mentally unsettled, unbalanced, and vacillating. I had been looking for support from a person who could offer me a panacea for living in our country. Lola had had such a prescription. She had been an iridescent butterfly bringing brilliant colour into my grey daily routine.

But now? I had overcome my own uncertainty. I no longer needed illusions in order to bear our harsh reality.

It was as though Lola had divined my own thoughts. Reading between the lines of her letter, it was clear that she too had undergone a transformation.

Dear Doctor [she wrote]. I promised to let you hear from me again. The time has now come to do so. During the past few months I had a lot of time for reflection. They were difficult months for me. Perhaps I shall tell you about them one day. Now I have found my feet again. I have become more serious and more mature. I hope we shall remain good friends, dear Doctor. If ever you should need my help, don't hesitate to let me know.

Sincerely yours,
L. O.

Into the margin she had crammed a postscript: "By the way, one can't always close one's ears to the radio."

8

BLISSFUL holidays! Four weeks of lying lazily among the dunes, by the surf and the sea. Far from the human suffering and the irritations of the hospital, from operating theatre and Casualty.

But in our country the State does not let its citizens off the leash even on holiday. Recreation and leisure are a strictly planned and highly organized business. There is no such thing as leaving matters to chance; there is no such thing as making plans. Anyone not allocated a holiday vacancy by March is excluded from the game altogether. Most people are told by the Free German Trade Union Federation where they may go for their holiday. We belonged to the few remaining 'free' holiday-makers, since we had been regular visitors for a number of years at a fisherman's cottage, where we took a room with bed and breakfast each summer. At least, we thought that we still belonged to that category as we drove through the pouring rain towards the Baltic coast.

It was an enjoyable drive, in spite of the monotonous rhythm of the windscreen-wiper. Ruth was gay and animated, talking about past holidays. Angelica was wriggling about on her lap, greeting every single cow that was standing in the sodden fields with a cheerful "Hello, moo-cow."

As an experienced holiday-maker, I had prepared myself for all eventualities. Nine gallons of petrol, in jerry cans, were stowed away in the back of the car, for we knew from experience that the filling stations were apt to run dry as the mighty stream of holiday-makers flowed towards the coast. The planned supply of petrol from the Leuna works was inadequate for the peak holiday demand at the seaside resorts. Our luggage moreover included several smoked salami sausages as our iron rations.

As we rounded the bend into our fishing village Ruth once again pulled out of her handbag the letter which the fisherman Twarstruff had sent us in February. He merely wrote to confirm that we could have our usual room again in July. It was in fact the matrimonial bedroom of Kai Twarstruff and his wife, Trine. During the holiday season they slept in a little living-room, and in this way made a small income on the side.

Kai Twarstruff's massive figure ducked through the door-frame of the ancient fisherman's cottage as our car came to a stop. His wrinkled face was tanned by the sea breeze. With the rolling gait of a seaman, he came forward to meet us.

"Don't start unloading yet, Herr Doktor," was his greeting. "I can't let the room to you this year. Everything's changed now. There are no free rooms nowadays."

"Well, what . . ." I was speechless with the shock.

"The Cultural League has requisitioned the room," he said. "They are now responsible for sending us our guests. But don't you worry. The local chairman of the Cultural League is a friend of mine. We'll just drive over to him and get the allocation chit. He's already promised me that he won't give the room to anybody else."

We drove over to the local schoolmaster, who was the chairman of the German Cultural League in the village. The League is a State-controlled organization for the intelligentsia. I was not a member.

The allocation was only a formality. The chairman of the Cultural League gave the rooms to all those who had already booked them. Nevertheless, the State now had absolute control over all holiday-makers. Even the last remaining private room had been requisitioned.

In addition to our accommodation chit, we also received vouchers entitling us to one hot meal per day. There were several housewives in the village who cooked for holiday visitors. We had our names put on the list of a widow we knew from past years, who provided dinners for fifty to seventy visitors each evening. Naturally, she did not have enough room for that number. So each family had its mealtime prescribed for them. After half an hour they had to clear the table because the next visitors were already waiting.

Experience from past years had taught us that the food was cheap enough, but also, as a result, rather insipid. That was not the fault of our widow. She had her prices prescribed for her, and at these prices she could not afford to serve anything out of the ordinary.

For that reason one of our first errands on the day of our arrival was to the only State-owned restaurant of the resort. Holiday visitors are usually hungry, and frequently find the official rations inadequate. But if a visitor still feels peckish after his voucher supper he cannot simply go to the restaurant and order a snack à la carte. The State-owned restaurant too has its regular customers with vouchers, for whom it supplies a hot meal at fixed times. Only when these regular guests have had their food can an outsider find room to sit down in the restaurant, and may then inquire humbly whether there is anything left to eat in the kitchen. For this purpose good relations must be established with the waitress. In return for a few friendly words, or better still a tip (although tips have been officially abolished in our country), she might be prepared to serve a fried egg and roast potatoes, or frankfurters with potato salad, at a late hour. But one can never rely on these supplementary meals, because sometimes the restaurant kitchen simply runs out of food. For those contingencies it is advisable to carry in one's luggage a salami and perhaps some bread.

The culinary highlights of a holiday on the Baltic used to be a dish of eel. Staying as we did with a fisherman, we were at the source of supply of those eels. In the past Frau Twarstruff used to give us eel *au bleu*—cooked in wine—at least twice during our four-weeks' stay. Now and again her husband would also get us smoked eel. Soon after our arrival I therefore alluded to the pleasant memories we had of eel dishes. But Twarstruff shook his square-shaped head. "There's no eel any more."

I smiled. Kai Twarstruff was rather fond of pulling the legs of landlubbers like ourselves. Perhaps his wife had an eel in her saucepan at that very moment, and was hoping to surprise us.

"Eels got too cunning for you, eh?" I asked. "Won't let themselves be netted by you any more?"

I waited in vain for the sly glint in his eyes. He thrust his hands into his pockets, spat, and looked grumpy. "They're letting themselves be caught all right. But you can't get any to eat any more. It's because of the production and marketing co-operative we've founded."

"A production and marketing co-operative?"

The collectivization of the peasants had just been completed: this very year the last of them had lost their farms. Now it seemed that the fishermen had suffered a similar fate. They were no longer free to sell what they caught. The catch belonged to the co-operatives. The co-operatives paid the fishermen for their work.

"But what happens to the eels?" I asked.

"The co-operative supplies them to the fish combines. After that they disappear. Probably exported."

I had begun to wonder why Twarstruff was at home more often now than he used to be. He was a reserved person, and did not speak his thoughts. But it was easy to see that he no longer got any pleasure out of his occupation. He did his eight hours and not a minute more. His parents and grandparents had been fishermen before him—lonely but proud people who wrested their livelihood from the sea, in their own boat and with their own nets. Kai had lost that freedom. He was not even allowed to take home an eel he had caught from his boat.

176

9

THREE days after our arrival another lot of visitors turned up at Kai Twarstruff's cottage. They too had been sent by the Cultural League. They were a sophisticated couple from Berlin, and belonged to the upper crust of our intelligentsia. Dr Gürtler was an art historian, and his wife a broadcaster. We met under the projecting roof of the cottage, as we were casting anxious eyes at the grey clouds which were far more numerous that July than they should have been. Holiday-makers are natural allies where the weather is concerned, and so we soon got into conversation. The Gürtlers belonged to that intellectual élite which was tolerated by the Party. They were interesting and stimulating company. As a result we spent much time together on the beach and, when the weather was bad, in the Twarstruffs' living-room.

We soon discovered that we had a mutual acquaintance. The Gürtlers spoke often about Lola Oehmichen. Only a week previously they had been to a party at her house. "A charming woman —clever and beautiful at the same time," Dr Gürtler raved. "She has collected around herself a circle of interesting and influential people. Actors, authors, Ministers, and leading figures of the State Security Service are among her regular visitors."

"She's back," his wife added more soberly. Her remark was not entirely devoid of envy. I did not want to ask any indiscreet questions—after all, we had not known the Gürtlers long enough. But I could only interpret Frau Gürtler's remark as meaning that Lola had only quite recently regained influence. Indeed, that was what she herself had hinted in her short letter to me. But had she experienced any unpleasantness in the intervening time? Had her husband kept her away from public life? Maybe from jealousy? Or had she got into conflict with the Party?

The following morning it so happened that I was alone with Frau Gürtler on the beach for a few minutes. Ruth had gone into the village to have her hair set, and Dr Gürtler had swum out into the bay. Angelica was making sand pies and decorating them with shells. I seized on the opportunity to ask Frau Gürtler about Lola.

"I've just heard from Frau Oehmichen again for the first time after many months' silence," I said to her. "It seems she has led a rather retired life lately."

Frau Gürtler was drawing circles in the sand with a stick, as Archimedes had once done. "Yes, very retired," she confirmed absently.

Two sentries from the frontier police, with binoculars round their necks and carrying sub-machine-guns, stumped past us through the sand. The two young men came from a fenced-off area in which stood a wooden watch-tower with radar aerials. Far out at sea a police launch was cutting a foaming arc through the silvery water.

"Was she ill?" I asked.

"Who? Oh—Lola. Oh, no."

"Did she have difficulties?" I persisted.

Frau Gürtler regarded me suspiciously. "I don't know," she replied with feigned indifference.

A boy of about twelve or fourteen dragged a rubber dinghy past us, and let it slip into the surf. "Would you mind keeping an eye on my things?" he asked us. Then he climbed into his dinghy and paddled away.

"You did not see Lola for quite a long time either?" I resumed my questioning.

She was gazing dreamily at the receding rubber dinghy. "No, I did not see her for a long time either," she said slowly. I sensed that she knew more than she wanted to tell me.

Her husband emerged from the sea, puffing and spluttering. A little while later Ruth turned up, her freshly set hair protected by a head-scarf from the sea breeze. "That's a smart launch out there," she exclaimed, pointing out to sea. There the police launch was streaking towards the boy in the rubber dinghy. He was a good distance out to sea now.

The frontier police hauled the boy into their launch. For a long time the police launch lay stopped at the same spot. Then it took the dinghy in tow and made for the beach at full speed. The police in the boat handed the boy over to a beach patrol. The patrol escorted him over to where his clothes were lying on the sand.

"Lot of nonsense!" the boy was saying angrily. "Attempted escape from the Republic in swimming-trunks and without papers?" To give them their due, the beach police did not seem to share the suspicion of their colleagues in the boat either. They did not treat the boy as roughly as they usually handle 'criminals.' They merely made him pick up his things and accompany them to the police station.

In the afternoon he was back on the beach. The absurd charge of attempting to escape from the Republic had, of course, collapsed. But in future the boy stayed closer inshore with his rubber dinghy.

Not until several days later did I find another opportunity of asking Frau Gürtler about Lola. While the others had gone ahead down the beach we had stopped at a poster hoarding to read an announcement inviting holiday visitors to attend a political lecture. 'West Berlin must become a free city,' was the subject. The speaker was that schoolmaster who was the local chairman of the Cultural League.

"*A propos* of Berlin," I said. "Will Frau Oehmichen return to her dancing again soon?"

This time Frau Gürtler was readier with her information. "No, she won't take on any further engagements," she reported. "That's one of the things she has since made up her mind about. I rather think that she had to promise it to her husband. The Under-Secretary has had a great deal of trouble because of her."

"Trouble?" I asked quickly.

"So it seems. But I don't know any details." For the rest of our holiday we kept off Lola. Frau Gürtler, I thought, was deliberately avoiding the subject. I felt sure that I should get no more information out of her.

Part Five

1

At the hospital they had been eagerly looking forward to my return. It was like a change of shifts. The first wave of holiday-makers was coming back and the second was getting ready to leave. On the stairs I ran into Paul Kranich. "You're too late, colleague doctor," he exclaimed. "Last night Comrade Werther made a speech here and really gave it to those warmongers and diversionists. You should have heard him! Don't miss reading his speech in the paper! Colleague Dr Kukowa was there too."

Kukowa was coming up the stairs behind me. I reached into my trousers pocket: I had brought him a paper bag full of sea sand, seeing that he had to do without a holiday.

At the same moment Professor Brunke came round the corner of the corridor and started down the stairs. He had a deep tan, and was looking younger than ever. He had spent his holidays by the Black Sea. With a jovial salute, he walked past us.

"Baltic sand!" Kukowa crowed delightedly. "I shall be able to use it for my holiday task, Herr Oberarzt."

Kranich and I looked at him inquiringly.

"It's still a secret, colleague Kranich," he said. "But if my experiments are successful I'll be made a Meritorious People's Doctor. As I'm not going away on holiday I'm going to grow radishes in my window-box—radishes which are red all the way through."

Kranich regarded him uncertainly. "Meritorious People's Doctor?" he asked reproachfully, as though Kukowa had just been making fun of a sacred concept. "By growing radishes?"

Kukowa acted mysterious. "I cannot disclose too much about it at the moment, colleague Kranich. But my research involves medical methods. Inoculation with human haemoglobin, for instance."

Paul Kranich suddenly discovered his sense of humour. "Could your method perhaps also be applied to human radishes—you know, colleague doctor, the comrades who are red on the surface only?" He giggled.

But Kukowa acted the offended scientist. "Colleague Kranich, you are laughing at my serious investigations."

Kranich was apologetic. "No offence, colleague doctor. I was only joking."

Kukowa followed me to my office. "You'll never go under in this country," I said, laughing.

He winked at me. "You may rely on it, Herr Oberarzt, the radishes will remain white inside."

In my office I found Sister Anneliese, with the wart on her nose. She was now temporarily in charge of my former ward also, since Sister Eva had stopped working because of her advanced pregnancy.

"Any new successes of the socialist brigade?" I asked Sister Anneliese.

She waved my question aside. "That brigade's only existed on paper ever since Ernst Pfeifer left us. Frau Piesewitz has stopped working for it too because she thinks her share of the May Day prize was too small."

On my morning round I missed Dr Ellen Tschauner.

"She was called by the Party," Kukowa announced. "At least, that's what the Regional Medical Officer told the chief when he asked him to excuse her absence. Last night, after the lecture of our dear comrade Werther, I saw her from a distance in the Melody night-club. But officially she is somewhere in Thuringia at a holiday camp of the Free German Youth."

In Ward 16 I expected to find hostile faces. Naturally the Sisters had told the patients that I was resuming my duties to-day. I felt pretty sure that Granny Novotny, as the oldest patient, would have told everyone else in the ward that Frau Brinkmann had been sent to a nursing centre because of my hard-heartedness. However,

Granny Novotny received me with a broad grin on her toothless mouth. It seemed we were friends again.

I inspected the wounds on her thigh. "Now, Granny Novotny, this looks a great deal better than it did ten weeks ago," I said. The ulcers had indeed healed a little along the edges, although complete success was still a long way off.

"It'll be all right again, Herr Oberarzt," she said casually. "But may I ask you a question?" I looked at her in surprise. "Herr Oberarzt, is it true that Herr Brinkmann has not yet been released from prison?"

"I've been away a long time, Granny Novotny, but I don't think he's been released yet," I said. She leaned forward excitedly. "You knew all about it at the time, Herr Oberarzt," she said. "I'm sure you knew all about it."

I evaded her question with some noncommittal phrase. Only with my eyes did I confirm that her assumption was correct. After that she trusted me again.

Dr Hansen was still on leave in Czechoslovakia, and was not expected back for another week. Jürgen Warberg, the 'living corpse,' was standing in for him. He seemed much more balanced and at ease now that he was not under Hansen's influence. Over the past six months he had also got used to working independently.

After my round I had to go to see my chief. Professor Zöllinger was getting ready for a holiday trip to Egypt, and had a lot to discuss with me. During the next four weeks I should have to run the department.

2

SISTER HELGA from the operating theatre had good news for me. Ever since that disastrous operation on Frau Steinkopf she had remembered my yearning for some needle-holders from West Germany. At last she had discovered a source. Herr Glas, the proprietor of the last specialized shop for surgical requirements, had still two needle-holders from Ulm in stock.

At the lunch-break I immediately drove out to the shop. Glas's was an old-established firm in our town; the father of the present proprietor had supplied my father with all his surgical instruments.

In the shop-window and on the shelves a few items were on display, emphasizing rather than concealing the shortage of everything. I found Herr Glas in his workshop, where, together with an assistant, he was bending over some repairs. "Yes, I still have two needle-holders manufactured in Ulm," he said, "but I'm not allowed to sell them to the hospital. I am only authorized to repair instruments belonging to the hospital. The hospital buys all its instruments from the German Trade Board, or occasionally from private owners."

Occasionally from private owners—that was my cue. "Are you allowed to sell the needle-holders to me, as a qualified surgeon, Herr Glas?" I asked.

"Yes, I am authorized to sell to doctors."

I asked him to keep the instruments for me and drove back to the hospital. I explained the situation to the administrator and asked his advice. The administrator, who used to be a printer and had spent much time learning the rules of our bureaucratic game, listened to me attentively.

"As for the first part of your story, colleague doctor," he said with a crafty smile, "I've already forgotten it. I don't have to investigate how the needle-holders came into your possession. You've only got to sign a declaration for me to the effect that you are the lawful owner of the instruments. Once we've got that the hospital is permitted to buy the needle-holders from you under the heading of occasional purchases from private persons."

By this roundabout route the transaction was concluded. I paid something like DM 150 to the dealer, and subsequently offered the instruments, now in my ownership, to the hospital. The hospital cashier then refunded me the sum that I had paid. It was a rather cumbersome procedure, but at least I now had some needle-holders on which I could rely.

Even more complicated was the purchase of a new car, on which I had decided. My daily journeys to the district hospital and my holiday trip had pushed up the total mileage of my Wartburg car to nearly 15,000. That with East German cars is the figure after which major repairs begin to be necessary. In fact, our return trip from the Baltic had been a bit of an adventure, since a suspicious tapping in the engine and an occasional clanking in the gear-box had set us wondering whether we should get back home safely.

The waiting-list at the State-owned motor shops was between twelve and eighteen months. But a doctor was entitled to priority. The salesman promised me a new Wartburg within three weeks at a price of just under DM 17,000. There is no difficulty at all in selling a used car. Industrial concerns, for instance, are not permitted to purchase new cars for their fleets of vehicles, and are instructed to meet their requirements with second-hand cars. As a result, they are only too glad to buy a vehicle from a private owner.

I therefore went along to see the chief accountant of the State-owned Fortschritt works and offered him my old Wartburg for DM 10,500. Officially a prospective vendor is not allowed to name a price, but it is nevertheless the common practice. Officially the value of a used car must be fixed by an authorized valuer from the Motor Vehicle Control Department. The idea is that these valuers will make sure that each party is treated fairly, and neither gains an improper advantage over the other. In actual fact, the valuers are a control organ of the State, designed to prevent the boards of State-owned factories from spending more of the money—which does not belong to them—than would be advisable. Private vendors as a rule demand high prices, and the accountants of enterprises do not offer enough resistance to these demands.

In my case, however, this system of safeguards proved ineffective. The chief accountant of the Fortschritt works was a close friend of one of the valuers. He rang him up in my presence and made it clear that the value of the car was to be fixed at DM 10,500.

I next drove the car into the yard of the Motor Vehicle Control Department. The valuer appeared, raised his eyebrows, pursed his lips, repeatedly nodded his head, and went through the motions of carefully assessing the advantages and disadvantages of the vehicle. He started the engine, tried out the brakes, made sure all the lights were working, and fell into profound meditation.

184

After a little while he solemnly announced his decision: "10,500 marks."

The sum was duly entered in the sales certificate and the various other car documents. Needless to say, I was allowed to keep my old car for the next three weeks, until my new one came along.

3

I HAD been back from my leave for about a fortnight when one lunch-time the Hospital Director's secretary rang through. Professor Brunke, she said, would be grateful if I could come round straight away for a minute.

The Director was sitting at his desk with a serious expression on his face, making notes on a case-history card. He picked up a stack of X-rays, thrust them at me, and asked: "What d'you make of those?"

I held up the negatives to the light. The spinal column and the pelvic bones were clearly recognizable. On the right side, towards the rear of the abdominal cavity, was a shadow the size of a bean. It could only be a stone. For a kidney stone it was too low. "A stone in the ureter, Herr Professor," I said.

Brunke stood up and walked round his desk to me. "Would you feel confident about removing it?" he asked.

I smiled. There are a great many more difficult operations than the removal of a stone in the ureter.

Brunke put his hand on my shoulders. "This is a rather special stone, you know—although of course the X-ray can't show that. It belongs to a very high Party official—a man who could easily have his operation at the Charité Hospital in Berlin, or even in Moscow. But he came to consult me because, to begin with, there was no indication that an operation might be necessary. The patient had been complaining of a troublesome pain on the right side of his abdomen. He has been in my department for the past fortnight. Drugs, unfortunately, have been useless. We have not succeeded in flushing out the stone. Our latest tests have shown that the kidney function is beginning to be affected. If we are to prevent lasting damage to the kidney the patient's got to be operated on during the next few days."

I said that I should give instructions at once for a private ward to be got ready in the surgical department, and that I should perform the operation as soon as possible.

Brunke was still acting very mysteriously. "I've said that he is a very high official. I should really have preferred Professor Zöllinger to operate on him. It would impress the Party rather more. But we can't wait until your chief returns. I don't want to pass him on to Leipzig, Jena, or Berlin either, because he is my patient and I want to look after him myself after the operation."

I rose to go back to the surgical department, to make the necessary preparations for the admission of a V.I.P. patient.

"Don't you even want to know who the patient is?" Brunke asked in astonishment.

"I hardly know the names of the senior Party officials," I replied coldly. "The name wouldn't mean anything to me."

"Oh, yes, it would. I remember you going rather sharply for him on one occasion. It's Max Werther, the Deputy Chairman of the Regional Committee. You'd better come along with me—I want to tell our patient that you'll take over the surgical treatment."

We walked down long corridors, past Dr Pollak's almost deserted sleep-therapy ward, and entered one of the recently restored private wards. It was empty.

Werther was sitting on a chair on the balcony, his legs crossed, reading a paper. He was wearing a well-pressed pair of trousers and a polo-necked pullover.

He immediately rose to his feet and greeted us courteously. He had forgotten my name, but he immediately remembered our clash at the doctors' meeting organized by the National Front.

"And now you want to operate on me?" he asked. He seemed to feel unhappy at the thought. "Isn't that a job that ought to be done by a professor?" he asked, turning to Brunke.

Professor Brunke, afraid of losing his important patient, put on his sales talk. "The *Oberarzt* here is an excellent surgeon. In fact, he has been temporarily in charge of another hospital, and is used to working independently. Besides, Herr Werther, men between thirty-five and forty have the steadiest hands. It's a well-known fact that they are the most skilful surgeons. That's the age when a surgeon makes a name for himself—a name on which he cashes in for the rest of his life."

Werther was scrutinizing me doubtfully. "I've nothing against you personally, Herr Doktor," he said. "I've only had one operation before, in 1947, and that was done by Sauerbruch. You know of him, of course—the greatest surgeon that ever lived in Germany. That's why I'm finding it a little difficult to decide."

I shrugged my shoulders regretfully. "I am no Sauerbruch," I said. "Nor do I wish to persuade you to let me operate on you."

Brunke gave me a reproachful look. But Werther intervened. "All right, then—I've already made up my mind. You do the operation—I have confidence in you. I remember very well that you took up the cudgels for your patients on that occasion. I was impressed by that. Have you managed to get good instruments? I can see to it at once that you get anything you need sent down from Berlin."

I declined with thanks. "No, thank you—we now have all the instruments we need." I should have loved to tell him what a complicated business the purchase of the needle-holders had been, but that would have taken too much time.

Max Werther reacted quickly. "I'll let you into a secret, Herr Doktor. Your arguments at the meeting impressed me so much that straight away I passed on your requests. I am delighted to hear that my intervention has been successful." Abruptly he grimaced and pressed his hand against his right hip. His intermittent pain had come on again.

We decided to have Werther moved to the surgical department the next morning. I promised to get our best private ward on the first floor of the theatre block ready for him.

4

Max werther brought with him a restless atmosphere. Early in the morning, even before the patient moved in, Professor Brunke turned up to inspect the room. He looked at everything, cursed because there was no balcony, had the bed pulled away from the wall because Werther—he explained—liked people to be able to walk round his bed. The couch and table, which I had specially borrowed from my chief's office, came in for a lot of criticism. In the end Ernst Pfeifer and another man from the outdoor staff had to bring over a settee and some chairs from Brunke's own office. Finally Brunke took a dislike to a large bunch of dahlias, which just then were cheap. He sent his own secretary into the town, because she was the only person he would credit with sufficient taste to choose flowers for a senior official.

Shortly afterwards Paul Kranich also turned up, a pile of newspapers and periodicals under his arm. With these he adorned one of the two bedside tables. Right on top of the pile he put *Neues Deutschland* and *Wochenpost*. Next came the local dailies and a few Berlin papers, and finally a number of brochures and pamphlets. Underneath this splendid selection of the literature churned out by our official printing presses Kranich had slipped two Westerns. He was indebted for this tip to the Cultural Affairs Secretary of the Regional Party Committee, who was familiar with Werther's tastes.

"A man's got to know the savage, rough-and-ready customs of our Colt-carrying enemies in order to appreciate fully the blessings of our socialism," Kukowa said appreciatively. When Kranich thanked him for this explanation of what had been to him an embarrassing task Kukowa immediately added a request for a few similar books for himself. But at that Kranich at once turned frosty again and left.

Werther's admission caused less excitement than I had expected. Bare-headed, the sick official crossed the hospital courtyard, followed by a nurse and a male nurse who were carrying his few pieces of luggage. I waited for him in the corridor, as Brunke had commanded, conducted him to his private ward, and introduced to him Sister Anneliese, who was going to be his private special nurse throughout his stay. This had been Matron's arrangement; some other Sister would meanwhile look after Sister Anneliese's ward.

The first visitors arrived that same morning. Large black limousines drew up outside the theatre block. The news that Werther was to have an operation had triggered off a wave of activity in the Regional Committee. One of the visitors who burst in while I was examining the patient was introduced to me by Max Werther as the Chairman of the Regional Committee of the Socialist Unity Party. So this was Peter Sachse, the highest representative of the regime in our province—a pale little man with prominent ears and a sagging lower lip. His vacant face was hidden behind thick horn-rimmed glasses. Sachse, as I knew from the newspapers, had been a member of the Communist leading clique ever since the twenties. As a young man he had already held important key positions in the Party; in 1933 he had emigrated to Moscow; he had taken part in the Spanish civil war; and he had gone to Russia, where he had been until 1945. With Pieck, Ulbricht, and the rest of the Party élite, he had returned as a Soviet citizen. Because of the aura which surrounded his name in Party circles he had been given the top post in our region, even though he was a quiet backroom type rather than a public figure. Into his hands converged the reins of power, and he kept a firm grip on those reins. But on public occasions, or if negotiations were to be conducted and speeches made, he would delegate these duties to Werther, a much more impressive figure than himself, and a man who was good at dealing with people. As a result, Werther was better known to the public than the more powerful Sachse.

The powerful Party boss asked me only a few trivial questions about the time of the operation and the probable length of Werther's detention in hospital. He did not seem too pleased that I, a man unknown in the Party, was to be in charge of the operation. His attitude to me was distant and condescending. It did not worry me, since at that time I did not think I should ever again have any dealings with him.

Still under Brunke's supervision, we continued for another two days our examinations and tests. Finally we took another X-ray, just to make sure the stone had not moved in the meantime.

The evening before the operation, when the routine work in the hospital had been done, I went round once more to see Werther. He had gone to bed on my advice because his pain had become worse. A young man with a low forehead and a square nose, evidently one of his closest collaborators, was still with him. Werther looked a little paler than during the day.

"It's a strange feeling, Herr Doktor," he said, "that one is to be cut open shortly. I'm not afraid of the operation, but I can't bear that dreadful smell of ether. And the whole business altogether. I hope I shall get a little sleep to-night."

"You'll sleep like a log," I said. "We'll give you a Kalypnon injection presently, and you'll hardly notice the smell of the ether, because we'll be giving you some Evipan beforehand. You'll wake up about lunch-time to-morrow, minus the stone. Soon you'll have forgotten all about it."

"Perhaps I'll have forgotten everything else as well," he said, with a forced smile.

When I tried to reassure him he stopped me. He did not want me to think that he was afraid for his life. "You know, Herr Doktor, it would be a heavy blow for the Party," he said, trying to suppress the tremor in his voice. "You met Peter Sachse, our Chairman this morning. He is an absolutely first-rate man in his post. But he does not understand public relations, or the problem of carrying the socialist idea to the masses. This is the great task that I have undertaken. And in this task I have already achieved some success, as Comrade Schubert here will confirm."

Comrade Schubert was only too eager to confirm whatever his master wished him to confirm.

"The Party will be facing its greatest tasks during the next few years," Werther continued. "It will be exposed to considerable strains and stresses, for we have not yet covered the most difficult sections of the road to socialism. The collectivization of agriculture was only a beginning. I don't want to trouble you with details, Herr Doktor, but you ought to know the value which the Party places on my life and good health. The burdens I bear cannot readily be undertaken by just anybody."

Comrade Schubert nodded. He was agreeing with everything that Werther, driven by fear, was saying.

Sister Anneliese came in with the Kalypnon injection. As I happened to be standing by the bed, I injected the tranquillizing liquid myself. I advised Werther to try to sleep and forget his worries. I personally escorted Comrade Schubert outside. I could not know that this short conversation was to have grave consequences for me.

5

Dr HANSEN, back from his holiday in Czechoslovakia, had offered to assist me at the operation. I politely declined, since I preferred Kukowa as first assistant. I realized, of course, that I was hurting Hansen's pride, for participation in an operation on a V.I.P. might have helped him a lot in Party circles. For my second assistant I had chosen the 'living corpse.'

Under the effect of Kalypnon, a tranquillizer manufactured and much used in East Germany, Max Werther had slept long and soundly. He had got over his anxiety when I paid him a short visit in the morning. We had fixed the operation for nine o'clock. He was wheeled into the theatre a little earlier, having had an injection of morphine and atropine. Atropine, one of the poisons of the deadly nightshade, inhibits bronchial secretion, which might otherwise occur when ether is used as an anaesthetic. Kukowa, the 'living corpse,' and I were meanwhile scrubbing-up. Kukowa, the first to finish, got an Evipan injection ready and injected it in the patient's arm. The Evipan we used was made in Hungary and supplied to us in a wrapping almost indistinguishable from that of the West German original. During the early post-war years there had been several fatalities with this imitated preparation, because the Budapest factory was not working under sterile conditions. Since those incidents, however, the quality had somewhat improved. The only thing that continued to annoy us was the shameless manner in which a West German patent was being exploited.

When Werther had fallen asleep under the effects of the Evipan Sister Helga asked in what position we wanted the patient. She wanted to know if the stone was in his right or left ureter.

"Silly question," Kukowa turned on her. "For a good socialist the enemy is always on the right."

Male nurse Bollmann turned the patient on to his left side and pushed a large pad under his hip. In this way the right side of his body was lifted a little and stretched, making it easier for us to operate. A woman medical auxiliary had meanwhile started an ether drip anaesthesia.

We three surgeons took up our positions. At nine o'clock punctually I was ready to make the first incision. Sister Helga passed me one of our best scalpels. I put its point down alongside the erector spinae muscle and made an incision above the iliac crest all the way round to the front of the abdomen. The incision ended parallel to the groin, and was about fifteen inches long. Three layers of muscles had to be cut through. There was a great deal of bleeding.

We now reaped the benefits of being a well-integrated team. Sister Helga was passing me the artery forceps even before I had asked for them. With these I caught hold of the bleeding arteries and closed them. Kukowa meanwhile divided the muscles. In this way we stopped all bleeding in a very short time.

"Raspatory."

Sister Helga was already holding it out to me. With it I loosened the layers of fat behind the peritoneum. The peritoneum itself did not have to be opened for this operation. The white cord of the ureter runs along the dorsal wall of the pelvis.

With large, blunt retractors we held back the sac of the peritoneum, which was trying to get into the way of the operation. I now laid bare the ureter as far as the renal pelvis. I then felt the whitish tube with my fingers, and on the spot where there had been a shadow on the X-ray I clearly distinguished some resistance. Here, then, was the stone which had been causing the patient pains for several weeks. I slipped blunt hooks under the ureter on either side of the stone. In this way the ureter was lifted from its base in two places. I asked Sister Helga for ligatures, and with them I tied off the ureter at the two points. This was done to prevent the stone from slipping away from the spot where it was lodged.

"Scalpel."

A small longitudinal cut in the ureter was all that was needed. We had previously put in two temporary sutures to prevent the tube from slipping out of place.

I now seized the ureter with my hand and squeezed the stone out through the slit we had cut, in much the way that toothpaste is squeezed out of a tube. Kukowa picked up the stone. It was the size of a bean, dark brown, and with a rough surface.

Sister Helga passed me the needle-holder with a curved needle and the catgut already threaded. It was a real pleasure to work with this needle-holder. It responded to the slightest pressure, and was so springy that the needle could not glance off even if handled by a beginner. I was glad I had made this purchase before the important operation.

The ureter was closed with four sutures. I examined the sutures once more, and was satisfied with my handiwork. So far everything had gone perfectly.

We placed four rubber drains alongside the ureter so that any fluid accumulating there could drain away through the skin of the patient's back. The large, blunt hooks, the retractors which had held the peritoneum away, were taken off again. The sac of the peritoneum slipped back over the area we had operated on. The rest was surgical routine. Three layers of muscle tissue to be stitched up again, fat tissue to be reconnected, skin to be sewn up, bandages to be applied. The whole operation had taken us exactly an hour.

We did two more operations that morning. Just as we had started on the last operation Frau Gummer appeared behind the plate-glass window in the anteroom, gesticulating furiously. I asked Sister Helga to find out what she wanted. The Sister opened the door. "The Chairman of the Regional Committee is on the telephone," Frau Gummer shouted. "He wants to speak to the *Oberarzt* at once."

"Please tell him that the operation has been quite satisfactory," I replied.

"But he wants to speak to you personally," Frau Gummer persisted. "It's Comrade Sachse himself."

I asked her to say I would ring him back as soon as I had finished operating. Not even the Chairman of the Regional Committee can expect a surgeon to interrupt an operation and hazard a patient's life.

Half an hour later, when I telephoned Peter Sachse, all he wanted to hear from me was what in fact Frau Gummer had already told him: operation satisfactory, no complications, patient in good condition.

6

SISTER ANNELIESE had a difficult time that afternoon. The patient, still drowsy from the anaesthetic, was feeling sorry for himself, and complained a lot. One moment he would whine that he wanted a drink, then he would want his pillow smoothed, then he would want the Sister to sit by his bed, and a moment later he would send her out of the room angrily. In these circumstances pampered men often behave like tetchy children. Werther was used to having his every wish fulfilled instantly, and he got annoyed when Sister Anneliese refused some of his requests.

Towards four in the afternoon Brunke came over to ask how the patient was doing after the operation. The surgical job had now been done, but it remained to be seen whether the affected kidney would recover its function, and whether the sutures on the ureter would hold. Brunke gave Sister Anneliese strict instructions. For the time being, needless to say, Werther was not allowed anything to drink. But once he was on fluids again she would have to enter the quantities on a chart, down to the last gramme. Brunke wanted an accurate check of the quantities of liquid going into the body and leaving it. In addition, he ordered regular blood tests, to make sure that the waste products which should be excreted through the kidneys did not accumulate in the blood.

Werther made a rapid recovery. On the following morning his eyes were clear, and he felt well enough to detain me for quite a lengthy conversation. Now that he had got over the operation he wasted no thoughts on the Party. He asked for his wife and his three sons to be notified that he would like them to visit him as soon as possible. In the course of the morning the square-nosed Comrade Schubert appeared with a large bunch of carnations and remained with his chief for a long time.

Frau Gummer was in her element. She was for ever on the telephone to some Party or Regional Committee offices, informing the comrades about the successful operation on the Deputy Chairman of the Regional Committee and about his steady improvement. Here was an opportunity to make contacts with many an influential comrade and to earn a good mark for herself. In her beautiful handwriting, she noted down on her memorandum pad all the names of the functionaries who sent their regards to Werther. For the time being she dissuaded the comrades from visiting the patient, but offered to make appointments for them for the next few days.

The tests of the patient's fluid balance and blood were very satisfactory. The damage done to the kidney by the obstruction of the ureter was disappearing rapidly. The ureter was healing up well along the suture. Werther had practically no pain now. For the time being, however, he could not move his arm. We had supported one of his arms on a stand shortly after the operation, opened the vein, and started a slow drip. Normal saline was steadily dripping into the vein from a bottle. This reduced the patient's feeling of thirst. We also introduced some alkaline solutions in the same way, to prevent over-acidity of the blood.

If there were a device to measure respect and courtesy I should have liked to wear it under my white coat during those few days. I have no doubt the pointer would have registered maximum. Paul Kranich, Frau Gummer, the Sisters, and the nurses all treated me with exquisite politeness, as though I had suddenly become an influential person. Dr Hansen came to my office one evening and congratulated me. "Your success has greatly impressed the Regional Committee," he told me, smoothing his hair with his palm. "Dr Tschauner, the Regional Medical Officer, has also asked about you. You are the next candidate for a *Chefarzt* vacancy."

I could not help smiling. "It really isn't very difficult to remove a stone from a ureter," I said. "As, of course, you know only too well, Herr Hansen."

He stared at me as if I were a rather obtuse child. "Surely what matters is not how difficult an operation is, but who benefits from it? You now have friends and supporters among the leading officials of the Party and the State. But you in turn ought now to leave no further doubt about your ideological attitude, Herr Oberarzt."

"Meaning?"

"You've got to demonstrate, Herr Oberarzt, that you're one of us. Most doctors shy away from committing themselves politically, and I confess that I too found it difficult at the time. But the Party expects us to give up our indifference. It has granted us doctors the privileged position which is our due. In return it demands, from the great majority of doctors, no more than a loyal attitude. But the élite, the men who will occupy the *Chefarzt* posts in the future, must come out clearly in favour of the Party's principles."

I still pretended I did not understand. "But I am coming out in favour of the Party's principles by the very fact that I am working in this hospital," I said.

"That's not enough. If you want to be a *Chefarzt*, Herr Oberarzt, you must become a candidate for Party membership. I shall be glad to give you what help I can, and propose your candidature."

I cut him off short. "Please don't trouble, Herr Hansen. I'll never become a Party member—never. None of my superiors has ever asked me to join the Party. If I am to get advancement in my profession I want it to be on the strength of my own ability."

Hansen got up and shrugged his shoulders. "Very well, Herr Oberarzt. Just as you please." He went out, sulking.

On the sixth day after the operation we were able to remove the rubber drains we had laid in the wound. We had already stopped the drip. Werther was in good spirits, and was continually receiving visitors. Peter Sachse also came twice and had a long conversation with him. After his second visit I met him in the corridor. He turned his expressionless face towards me. "That's a fine job you've done, Herr Oberarzt," he said, without any inflexion in his voice. "I hope we shall hear more of each other. I don't suppose you want to remain at this hospital for ever."

He had an unpleasant manner of speaking, cold and impersonal. I smiled as I watched him leave, accompanied by Comrade Schubert. I was enjoying the benevolent attention of the Party because I had successfully performed a perfectly ordinary ureterolithotomy. I had only to apply for membership, and I should be assured of a dazzling career. I was more firmly determined than ever not to take this step.

7

I HARDLY knew Frau Gummer when, on the ninth day after Werther's operation, I walked into Casualty. Her little grey eyes positively sparkled in her wrinkled face. "What d'you think, Herr Oberarzt—our Sister Eva has had her baby! A bonny boy, weighing seven pounds. He's called Ernst, like his father."

I was reminded of that day in January when Sister Eva had first confessed to me that she was expecting a baby.

Unfortunately, this was to be the only good news that morning. Sister Anneliese was waiting for me in the corridor to tell me that Werther had woken up with sharp pains. His temperature was up to over 100. I slipped on my white coat and went straight to his room. Werther was lying on his left side, gritting his teeth and groaning. He had a pain in the right side of his abdomen. "It feels as if something has burst," Werner panted.

All signs indicated an inflammation. More than that it was

impossible to say at the time. I decided to treat the patient with Chloronitrin, an antibiotic manufactured in East Germany, and our most powerful weapon against bacteria. But I was fighting against the invisible causes of a yet unidentified infection. It was a rare complication after an operation. We had worked as cleanly as always, and used better instruments than most times. But there is no complete safeguard against such incidents.

The stream of visitors, fortunately, had somewhat abated during the past few days. Those who came were turned away by Sister Anneliese. "A slight setback in his recovery," she said regretfully. "Herr Werther is not feeling as well to-day as usual." It sounded harmless, but it was enough for Peter Sachse—who had been instantly informed—to send two officials to me. They wanted to know if I needed any West German or American medicines for Werther. It was too early to tell whether the Chloronitrin would be effective against the infection, but just to be on the safe side I asked for a small quantity of broad-spectrum antibiotics from the West—antibiotics simultaneously effective against a wide range of bacteria. A special courier was sent off to Berlin the same day.

The patient's temperature continued to rise during the afternoon and evening. Chloronitrin was evidently not clearing up the infection. The symptoms were beginning to add up to peritonitis.

It was a hot and sticky day. The summer, until then cold and rainy, was making up for past neglect with sultry, thundery heat. In the operating theatre we sweltered in our hoods, masks, and gloves. For the past week I had been looking after two wards, as the 'living corpse' had been detailed as a camp doctor to a holiday camp of the Free German Youth. Ellen Tschauner was not due to return to duty for another two days.

Whenever I had a spare moment I looked in on Werther. The first phase of an inflammation is usually the one where the best effect can be achieved with drugs. The crisis was still ahead.

The next morning the courier returned from the Government Polyclinic Dispensary in Berlin. He brought with him several packets of aureomycin and terramycin capsules. Werther inspected the golden-yellow powder in the transparent capsules with interest; it looked like honey-coloured pollen. "American?"

he asked. I confirmed his guess, and told him the preparations had been obtained specially for him. "Why the hell can't our Meritorious People's Inventors produce stuff like this?" he grumbled. "It's disgraceful that we should still have to rely on the Americans for all the best medicines."

In point of fact our home-produced Chloronitrin had proved ineffective against his condition. On the second day his temperature was higher than on the first. The centre of infection had spread. But Werther was more optimistic than on the first day. We dulled his pain a little by giving him medicines which slightly clouded his consciousness. Besides, his feverish condition was weakening him, and saving him from fear and introspection. He had every faith in the effectiveness of the American preparation.

However, there was no perceptible improvement on the third morning. The patient did not touch the delicacies which were specially produced for him in order to keep up his strength. Two new Westerns, which Paul Kranich had dug up from somewhere, had been lying unread on his bedside table for the past two days. Nor did he look at the newspapers brought in every morning. He lay listless, and slept a good deal. But as soon as anybody moved about the room he would wake up and speak to us. "How long does this sort of thing take, Herr Oberarzt?" he asked, when I looked in on him at lunch-time.

"You've now reached the turning-point," I answered. "Your temperature will go down again during the next few days. But you'll have to stay with us for at least a fortnight."

"I don't think I can afford that," he growled. "To-morrow is the 28th of August. Correct? I was to make a memorial speech for Ernst Thälmann. He was murdered at the Buchenwald concentration camp on August 28, 1944. Now someone's got to take my place."

August 27, the day of this conversation, was a Saturday. Strictly speaking, I was to have been off duty that afternoon and the following Sunday, but I had exchanged shifts with a colleague, and undertaken to be on call for the weekend. Otherwise, if Werther's condition did not improve, I could have come in for criticism afterwards.

At noon on Saturday Sister Anneliese was relieved by Nurse Karin, a probationer, who was likewise a member of the socialist brigade. In the early evening, as I was catching up with some paper-work in my office, Nurse Karin burst in excitedly. Would I please come and see Herr Werther at once? she panted. When I entered his private ward I saw male nurse Nitschke holding him down with both hands.

"Class enemy! Traitor to socialism! Saboteur!" Werther was shouting. "I'll have you arrested. I've got to go and make my speech. Ten thousand workers are waiting for me."

I tried to calm him, and pressed him back into his pillows. I told him he was ill. He must wait for the American drugs to take effect. The workers' meeting was not until to-morrow, and then some other speaker would take his place.

"You're an enemy of the State, comrade!" he screamed at me. "You're only disguised as a doctor. Did you know Ernst Thälmann? You're trying to keep me here. I know perfectly well I'm all right. Why do you keep telling me I'm sick?"

He took some time to calm down. Nitschke ran down to Casualty and came back with belts for strapping Werther to his bed. He allowed himself to be strapped down without opposition. In his delirium he no longer saw us. He was keeping up a dialogue with the dead Ernst Thälmann. He was complaining to the old comrade about the new comrades. He was running through a long list of mistakes which were now being made. Every sentence he uttered, at the bidding of his subconscious, would have got him into trouble with the State Security Service.

Male nurse Nitschke, who had had his chemist's shop confiscated by the Communists, thoroughly enjoyed the high Party official's heretical remarks. I too would have enjoyed his involuntary confessions, had I not been listening to them with a doctor's ears. The very fact that the patient was delirious was highly disturbing. It indicated that the disease was progressing, and that its advance had not been checked by the aureomycin either.

The following morning I was able to have a normal conversation with Max Werther. He was very weak and limp, but answered my questions lucidly. He had no pain. He was only troubled by thirst. Nurse Karin had to moisten his lips at frequent intervals. When I gave him another capsule of antibiotics he smiled gratefully. "Yes, they're doing me good, Herr Oberarzt," he whispered. "I can feel it."

About noon his mind became clouded. He slipped into a state of unconsciousness. The large number of visitors who came to see him that afternoon were allowed to his bed only for a minute or so. He took no notice of them, even when now and then he opened his eyes. Only when his wife spoke to him did he nod and move his lips. His mind was already in another world.

But his heart was still pounding. It was full of energy, and sense-lessly pumped his blood through his veins. Not till Monday night did it begin to flag. The weakened body no longer struggled in agony. All the night Sister heard was a soft sigh. When she stepped up to his bed Max Werther was dead.

8

THE post-mortem showed that a contusion had formed in the area of the operation, that it had become septic, and burst through the peritoneum. I watched over the pathologist's shoulder. "It's just terribly bad luck," he said to me when he had established the cause. "Certainly there's been no mistake of any kind."

Professor Brunke was the first to have the pathologist's report submitted to him. He was sorry that the case, which had looked harmless enough at first, should have taken such a tragic turn. It certainly was a poor recommendation for the hospital that a senior official should have died of an ordinary stone in the ureter. But Brunke did not reproach me in the least. He knew the many pitfalls in the face of which a doctor is powerless. "This piece of bad luck after a perfect operation could just as easily have hap-pened to Professor Zöllinger," he said.

The Party staged a spectacular funeral for Max Werther. I was unable to attend, because on Thursday morning two gentlemen appeared at the hospital and asked to see me. I had just finished the first operation on my list when Frau Gummer asked me to come out into the corridor. The two strangers regarded me steadily. "There are a few questions that want clearing up, Herr Doktor," one of them said. "We should like you to accompany us to the Regional Committee Office."

I objected that I had two more operations to perform. But the stranger replied, politely yet firmly, that this was an important matter, and I should have to leave the operations to another surgeon. I instructed Hansen to stand in for me, washed my hands, and took off my theatre overall.

I was completely cool and calm at that moment. It certainly looked as if I was being arrested. Outside the main entrance stood a black Sachsenring saloon with a chauffeur. The man who had addressed me in the corridor politely stood aside to let me get in first, and sat down next to me on the back seat. The other sat in front.

"Who wants to see me?" I asked the man by my side, though I hardly expected to get an answer.

But the man lit a cigarette, offered me the packet, and said absently: "Comrade Sachse, Herr Doktor. He wants to ask you some questions. I'm not quite sure what it's all about."

I drew an audible sigh of relief. Only now did my hand with the cigarette begin to shake. My first idea had been that the men must be from the State Security Service. Their suspicious hurry, the black Sachsenring saloon, the mere fact that two men had been sent to pick me up—all that had seemed significant. Surely, if he had merely wanted me to call on him for a few minutes, Peter Sachse could have used the telephone?

We were driving towards the city centre. There, amid a bomb-flattened expanse, stood the new building of the Party Regional Committee. But only one block farther on was the building of the former Law Courts which now housed the State Security Service. My neighbour had fallen silent again. Was he after all a Security man? The building of the Party Regional Committee now appeared on our left. On its roof the flags were at half-mast. In a moment the driver would have to turn left if he were really taking me to Party headquarters. Now he would have to slow down. But he drove straight on. He drove past the building, with its ornate façade. So it was the State Security Service after all. And now he was really slowing down. He made a U-turn round a traffic island, swung off the roadway, and pulled up outside the Party building.

I could have kicked myself. Why was I so jumpy? My companion had told me that Peter Sachse wished to speak to me. What was so incredible about that? I had operated on his deputy. I had been looking after him to the end. It was perfectly natural that Sachse should wish to hear a few more details about Max Werther's last days from the doctor in charge.

My companions took me to a room on the first floor and left me there. It seemed to be a waiting-room for visitors, for lying on a low table in the centre were newspapers and much-thumbed periodicals. I settled down in a corner seat and read.

Half an hour passed. If they were going to keep me waiting that long, I thought, I could have finished operating.

At last one of my companions returned. "The Chairman of the Regional Committee will see you now," he said formally, and opened the door. I entered a vast room, where the slight Peter Sachse seemed almost lost behind an enormous desk. In the background sat six more men, of whom I knew only the square-nosed Comrade Schubert. Peter Sachse shook hands with me casually and pointed to a chair. He did not introduce to me the men in the background. His eyes in the expressionless face were looking past me as he invited me, in his impersonal manner, to tell him about Max Werther's last days and the cause of his death.

I had regained my composure. I looked straight at Peter Sachse's expressionless white face, focusing in turn on his sadly drooping lower lip, his thick horn-rimmed glasses, and his prominent ears. As lucidly as I could, and with very few medical terms, I explained to him Werther's illness. Peter Sachse was not greatly interested in the kidney stone which had descended into the ureter and got stuck there. He was far more interested in how contusions were caused.

I explained to him that contusions were by far the most frequent form of injury known to us. "They are what in ordinary life we call a bruise. They are caused when a blood-vessel is damaged by a blow, sudden impact, or in any other way, and the blood oozes from it into the surrounding tissue. Every operation in which blood-vessels are damaged is in a sense an artifically caused contusion. In nearly all cases the blood that has oozed out is absorbed by the tissue within a few days, and no adverse consequences remain."

"But in Max Werther's case this did not happen?" Sachse asked.

"In his case, as we subsequently established, some sources of infection settled in the bruised tissue, causing suppuration. This produced large quantities of pus, which eventually penetrated through the peritoneum into the abdomen and poisoned it."

Sachse made me repeat my explanation several times. He asked a great many questions, wanted to know details, inquired about the meaning of medical terms, and in between allowed such prolonged pauses to occur that I thought the interview was at an end on several occasions.

The men in the background sat silent, listening. Not one of them smoked. I wanted to light a cigarette, but at the last moment noticed that there was not an ash-tray in the room. Evidently Peter Sachse was a non-smoker, and did not like his office filled with tobacco smoke.

"Well, I'm finding all this very difficult to understand," he said in conclusion. "Can you explain why this sort of accident should happen to, of all people, one of the most important men in the Party?"

"Nobody can explain that," I said.

"Did you know what an important position Max Werther held in the Party? Did you know anything about him?"

"No," I replied guilelessly.

But here Comrade Schubert intervened. "That's not so, Comrade Sachse," he exclaimed eagerly. "On the evening before his operation Comrade Werther deliberately mentioned to the doctor his important rôle in the Party. He told him quite a few details about his work. I was present myself."

Almost unnoticeably the medical consultation had turned into an interrogation. They had set a trap for me, and I had blundered into it.

"It's quite true," I admitted, "that on the evening before his operation Herr Werther told me that he was indispensable to the Party. He was a little nervous of the operation, like most patients. It's quite natural that one does not want to be left alone with one's anxiety, but tries to make conversation with one's doctor."

Now a man with cold, narrow eyes and hard lines around his mouth joined in: "You were saying, Herr Doktor, that the patient was anxious. Was there any reason for his anxiety?"

I was beginning to find the questions frightening. "I have said already that nearly every patient is afraid of an operation," I repeated.

"Did Herr Werther ever say anything to you about not wishing you to operate on him?" the man with the narrow eyes persisted.

"He was reluctant the first day," I said, "but his misgivings were not about my person but about my position. In 1947 Herr Werther was operated on by Professor Sauerbruch, and he would have preferred to have a very prominent surgeon again."

"So he did voice his misgivings?"

"Only during our first conversation."

"Never mind, Herr Doktor. You admit that he did voice them?"

I shrugged my shoulders. "I'm no Sauerbruch. Why shouldn't he have misgivings about being operated on by an unknown *Oberarzt*?"

There was some movement about Peter Sachse's lips. For the first time I saw the suggestion of a smile on his expressionless face. "Werther never questioned your professional skill. Neither, for that matter, did I. I told you that much in the corridor at the hospital the other day. But can you think of any other reasons why Werther should not wish to be operated on by you?"

I looked at him uncomprehendingly. They were all staring at me.

"If you can't think of one then I shall have to tell you," Sachse continued, without raising his voice. "Last March, in the course of a discussion with National Front officials, you had a clash with Werther. You attacked him sharply because, so you said, not enough was being done for the patients in our hospitals. The manner of your attack was bound to create the impression that you do not recognize the principles of socialism."

"You have been misinformed, Herr Sachse," I said simply. "There was no question of a sharp attack; it was a discussion in which we were asked to voice our requests. I drew Herr Werther's attention to the fact that several important instruments were lacking in our hospital, and that others were no longer up to requirements and would need replacing by new ones. I also said that improvements were needed in our supply of medicines. Herr Werther accepted my suggestions and promised to help. That was all."

"That was all," Peter Sachse repeated after me. "Well, now, Herr Doktor; we shall have to continue our conversation in the afternoon. Please regard yourself as the guest of the Regional Committee. Comrade Schubert, with whom you are acquainted, will look after you and take you to lunch."

This concluded our conference. Schubert offered me a chair in the little room where I had waited before, and replenished the stock of papers with the latest dailies. He kept me waiting for an hour and then took me to another room where lunch was served for the two of us.

We ate in silence. Schubert did not address me, and I saw no reason for making conversation with him. With the simple meal I also swallowed my cold anger. What did these people want with me? Did they seriously think there had been any personal animosity between Werther and myself? Did they think I had let Werther die deliberately? The very idea was absurd.

After lunch Schubert offered me a cigarette. I asked him how long the conference was likely to take that afternoon. "That depends on you, Herr Doktor," he said coldly. "If you just explain to Comrade Sachse why Max Werther died it need not take long."

I flushed. "Does anyone believe I bungled the operation? Haven't they seen the pathologist's report?"

Comrade Schubert was unmoved. "I don't know what the comrades believe. But they want to learn the truth from your own lips. Why don't you tell them what really happened?"

He did not leave me time for an answer, and led me back to the waiting-room. I asked him if I could ring up the hospital. "When the conference is over," he decided. "They might want you any moment now."

I was kept waiting again. I smoked. After a while Schubert came back and led me down several corridors and stairs to a small conference room. On one side of the long table sat Sachse, the man with the narrow eyes, and several other men whom I did not know. Two of them had not been present in Sachse's office that morning. Next to Peter Sachse sat a young man with sparse hair. In front of him on the table was a stack of foolscap paper. I discovered presently that he was taking down a record of the interview.

This time it was a full-dress interrogation. I was asked the same questions that I had already answered that morning. But they were formulated rather more sharply, and implied clearly that I was expected to confess to having had differences of opinion with Werther before the operation. They were trying to get me to admit that I would have regarded Werther's death as a serious and irreparable loss to the Party. Finally, yet another point began to crystallize: so far I had shown no signs of wishing to co-operate in building socialism in our country. It might therefore be concluded that I was more interested in weakening than in strengthening the Party.

In the end I was asked if I wished to comment clearly and un-equivocally on these accusations. I rose to my feet and looked rigidly at Peter Sachse: "From all the questions put to me I con-clude that I am to be accused of allowing Herr Werther to die deliberately. To this I can only reply that a full autopsy report is available. I am, moreover, prepared to answer any questions asked of me by a committee of doctors."

This concluded the afternoon session. However, I was not yet allowed to return to the hospital, but was taken back by Schubert to the small waiting-room. I was kept waiting there for another hour. At last Peter Sachse, accompanied by Schubert and the narrow-eyed man, came in. "The accusation of letting Werther die deliberately has not been made against you, Herr Doktor," Sachse said. "In fact, the Party has not made any charge against you. But you must feel yourself that the questions we discussed this afternoon are by no means clarified yet. Some further discussions will be necessary. I am asking you therefore to go with this gentle-man"—he pointed to the narrow-eyed man—"who will take down a new statement from you." He nodded to me briefly and slouched out.

In the corridor outside we were joined by the silent man who had sat next to the chauffeur on our drive to Party headquarters that morning. Outside a black saloon was again waiting for us. This time I had no doubt where we were going. Two minutes later we drew up outside the building of the State Security Service.

9

THE man with the narrow eyes conducted me to a square room in which were a table, some chairs, and a bed. "I'm afraid we shall have to trouble you to spend the night with us because we intend to resume work early in the morning, and are unable to tell you to-night at exactly what time we want to see you to-morrow," he said politely.

The room was furnished simply, but did not look like a cell. On a shelf on the wall were papers and books, and on the table (which was covered by a rather small and not entirely clean cloth) stood an ash-tray. The door had not been locked behind me, and the windows were not barred. Nevertheless, I felt that I was being closely watched.

If only I could have telephoned Ruth! No doubt they had rung her up from the hospital to tell her I had been picked up for questioning. She was bound to be worried—much more than myself. Although I knew that I was in for some tough questioning, I was composed and calm. There can always be some argument as to whether a doctor has done everything to save a patient. Malicious people can always claim afterwards that this method or that should have been tried at the last moment. But the attempt to accuse me of deliberately killing a Party official was ludicrous.

Even so, I slept badly that night. I was not used to sleeping in a room with the light full on. I lay awake for hours, smoking and browsing through the books on the shelf. I ran out of cigarettes. During the ordeals ahead I should miss them.

Towards seven in the morning I was woken by a warder who brought me some soap and a towel. Behind a grey curtain was a hand-basin and a tap.

"What would you like for breakfast, Herr Doktor?" the man asked. "Coffee or tea—a boiled egg? Is there anything else you'd like? Cigarettes, or anything we could buy for you?"

I gave him a five-mark note and asked him to get me some cigarettes. The service could not have been better in a first-class hotel. On my breakfast-tray was a daily paper. "You've got plenty of time to have breakfast in comfort, Herr Doktor," the friendly warder said. "The first conference with you isn't till nine o'clock."

Only two well-dressed men and a shorthand writer were present during this conference. I was asked, politely and in a business-like manner, about my professional training and career, about my position in the hospital, and about my duties as a factory doctor. It was a conversation rather than an interrogation. After an hour I was taken back to my room.

A second, similar interview took place shortly before lunch. This time the questions were about my political activities, and about my membership in clubs and associations.

In the afternoon the narrow-eyed man suddenly came for me. He took me to a bare room which contained only a table and three chairs. Two of these were already occupied by strangers. The narrow-eyed man sat down on the third. I had to remain standing in front of the table.

One of the two strangers stared at me as if he wanted to kill me with his looks and said sharply: "A second post-mortem has shown that during the operation chemicals were used which irritated the peritoneum. Will you tell us yourself what you used, or do you want us to tell you?"

I had not expected such a clumsy bluff. I tried hard to remain calm. "Would you please show me the second autopsy report?"

"It's still being written up," said the man with the narrow eyes. "It'll be shown to you presently. What chemicals did you use to produce the subsequent inflammation?"

"I am a doctor, not a murderer," I said coldly.

The first speaker, who was in charge of the interrogation, brought his palm down hard on the table and leapt to his feet. "Kindly answer the questions," he shouted at me. He went on shouting and hammering the table with his fists. I reminded him that two assistants, two Sisters, one nurse, and one medical auxiliary had been present throughout the operation. It would have been quite impossible for me to make a single unobserved move.

He interrupted me angrily. "Nobody is saying that you used illicit means with evil intent," he said, a little less hostilely than before. "But something must have got into the wound, possibly without intent, which eventually produced the infection. Surely you ought to be as anxious as ourselves to clear up this matter as quickly as possible. If only you were more co-operative you could be back in your hospital this afternoon."

I merely shrugged my shoulders and repeated my earlier replies. "Very well," the man in charge said eventually. "You will have an opportunity of discussing these questions with us in the presence of doctors in a few days' time. I am very sorry that we shall have to keep you with us until then."

I was taken back to my room and left alone. Suddenly I felt very depressed. For the first time I realized my helplessness. I was at the mercy of these men. They could do whatever they liked with me. Several more times, during the late afternoon and the evening, I was fetched back for further questioning. The operation itself was no longer discussed. The questions were all about personal relations, my attitude to the Party, my views on socialism. I answered all questions mechanically. They had very little to make a charge stick. My behaviour in recent years had been correct throughout, or, as the Party puts it, 'loyal.'

On the following morning the picture changed. I was no longer asked what I wanted for breakfast, but was simply given malt coffee and two slices of dry bread. An obese man with a bald head and a fat face was in charge of the first interrogation. From the way he spoke to the narrow-eyed man and the third man present I concluded that he himself held a higher rank. The proceedings were rather more bureaucratic and conventional than on the previous day. The bald-headed man had several folders lying on the table before him. I was again offered a chair. For nearly half an hour my personal data were taken down. Several times the bald-headed man deliberately emphasized my middle-class background to make sure it got into the record. Then he asked me abruptly: "When and where did you meet Heinz Becker during the past few weeks?"

I looked at him, startled.

"Don't stop to think. It'll only be held against you. We have proof that Heinz Becker spent two days in the German Democratic Republic just before the operation. Don't try to deny that you've been in touch with him."

Now I really did not know what to say. Heinz Becker had been a fellow-student of mine, and had been sentenced to a long term of imprisonment in 1950 on charges of activities hostile to the State. At the trial then I had tried to give evidence in his favour. I had not seen him since. I did not know whether or when he had been released from prison. He certainly never got in touch with me again. Ten years had elapsed since that terrible trial, but my testimony for the defence had evidently gone into the records of the State Security Service. All sorts of details from the testimony given by me then were now being quoted back to me. Most of them had escaped my memory.

From the bald man's questions and hints I concluded that Heinz Becker had escaped from the country some years ago and, in the opinion of the State Security Service, was now a member of a West German espionage organization. The Security people claimed to know that he had visited our country under a false name several times, the most recent just before Werther's operation.

I was in a very nasty spot. At first, I supposed, Sachse and his comrades had merely intended to investigate the possibility that I might have caused Werther's death through negligence or deliberately. As a matter of routine, they had simultaneously inquired with the State Security Service whether there was anything against me on their files. And from their archives they had unearthed the fact that I had been a witness for the defence in Heinz Becker's trial.

Whether or not Heinz Becker had really been seen in East Germany two days before Werther's operation I do not know. To-day I consider it possible that the Security people were merely bluffing. But once they had discovered this tenuous connexion they made it a focus of their questions. Perhaps they really thought it possible that I had been hired by enemy agents to liquidate Max Werther in a manner that would not arouse suspicion.

Hour after hour the interrogations continued. Several times the bald-headed man was relieved by the narrow-eyed one. Again and again the same questions were put to me. One moment they would be friendly, offer me cigarettes, and conduct the conversation in almost a chatty tone, and the next moment they would scream at me and abuse me. In the early afternoon there came a pause in the questioning. As for the friendly room where I had first been accommodated, I never saw that again. The warder took me to a bare cell without windows. A naked lamp hanging down from the ceiling filled the small, dismal room with a dim light. From now on it was clearly intended that I should feel myself a prisoner of the State Security Service.

There was no question now of a temporary stay for the elucidation of certain questions. I could expect weeks or even months of investigations.

I sat down on the creaking bed and hid my face in my hands. I was in despair. What every citizen in our country was afraid of had now happened to me. I had never believed that it could happen to me. True, I had done nothing for the Party, but likewise I had done nothing against it. Millions of people lived the kind of life I had lived. They did their job, enjoyed their leisure, and erected a glass wall between themselves and politics. They did not love the State, but they observed its laws. And yet one fine day it reached out for them, as it had reached out for me.

Worst of all were the long waits: humiliated and abused, one's stomach wrung by fear of the unknown. Alone and utterly lonely, hoping for a miracle.

The warder came in to take me to another interrogation. Again I was faced by the bald-headed man with the fat face. This time he wanted to know about my connexions with people who had fled the country. He questioned me about every single doctor from our hospital who had escaped recently.

"You were a close friend of Dr Busch?"

"Yes."

"Dr Reger was a good friend of yours?"

"Yes."

"In both cases you knew that these men intended to escape from the Republic?"

"No."

"Don't lie!"

The questions and accusations beat down upon me like hail. I had to admit that I was still in correspondence with both my friends.

"Last March you had a strange telephone call from West Berlin."

I reflected. "A patient."

"What's the patient's name?"

"I should have to look it up in my card index."

"Is that so?"

As I had feared, Lola's call had been listened in to. I remembered clearly that she had not uttered a single compromising word. Most certainly I could not now reveal her name. The bald-headed man made a note. Presumably he would ask further questions about the unknown caller later.

The interrogation continued. The bald man named two escaped doctors of whom I had never heard. He was staring at me like a hypnotist. But my conscience was clear, and I did not move a muscle in my face. By means of a great many cross-questions about these two doctors he presently tried to trap me. In the end, it seemed, he realized himself that he was on a false trail.

"You're not going to tell us the name of the caller from Berlin?"

"I'd like to tell you, but I don't know it off-hand."

"The caller said verbatim: 'Don't forget the force of destiny.' What's the meaning of this code?"

"It's an opera by Verdi," I said guilelessly.

"Don't you act an opera to us!" he shouted at me. "I want to know the meaning of it."

I felt burning anger rising inside me. But I had to keep calm. Think, think!

"The patient was very ill," I said. "I had to encourage her because I wanted to use her will-power as a factor in my treatment. I told her that it was her destiny to get well again. Verdi's opera *The Force of Destiny* was a favourite of hers."

The bald man grinned. "You thought that one up a little too quickly, Herr Doktor. Would you mind explaining to me why your patient had to remind you by telephone of the force of destiny, instead of you reminding her? Or had *you* fallen ill in the meantime?"

"No, but . . ."

"Don't try to lie—anyone can see when you are lying. The fact that this call contained a coded message for you is obvious to the most inexperienced interrogator. You were in touch with certain quarters in West Berlin, who on that particular day had an important reason to warn you. Even at the risk that the conversation would be monitored. Correct?"

"No, it's not correct," I persisted.

"We shall have plenty of time to talk about it again."

Back to my dismal cell. This time with a nagging feeling that I was not equal to those hard-boiled police. I had to lie now in order to get out of the noose. Until then I had been able to deny everything with a clear conscience. For the first time the bald man had noticed that I was lying. He would make the most of his discovery.

Towards six in the evening the warder came for me again. This time he took me to a small office where the narrow-eyed man was sitting behind a desk. "Would you be kind enough, Herr Doktor, to sign this declaration?" he said in the most courteous tone. I looked at the document. In it I undertook to keep strict secrecy about anything I had heard or seen in the building. Any infringement of this undertaking would have serious consequences for me. Then he got up and shook hands with me. "I'm very grateful to you for helping us to clarify those few outstanding questions. The matter is now closed. All the best, Herr Doktor."

I felt as if I had drunk a bottle of champagne. I was free again, I could go wherever I wished—I could hardly believe it yet. I walked along the familiar streets of the city centre. There was the Town Hall with its bomb-damaged tower; over there was the building of the Regional Party Committee. Surreptitiously I looked behind me to see if there really was no one following me. No; I was free. Free! I probably could have found a taxi in the city centre. But I had to walk home. I simply had to walk—walk freely wherever I wished to go. It had all been like a bad dream. Only a few minutes ago I had seen no way out. I had expected weeks and months of torture. And suddenly it was all over. It really was like waking up from a nightmare.

I rang our front-door bell three times. Ruth burst out and swept me into her arms. She did not say anything. She did not have to say anything. She was crying.

10

I PUT a bottle of Tokay on the table. This evening belonged to Ruth and me. Angelica was still rattling the bars of her cot and crowing: "Daddy back, Daddy back." Ruth was laughing, and tears were running down her cheeks. "I'm sorry," she sobbed. "Three days and two nights worrying about you—that was too much."

She did not ask for details. Kukowa had brought her the news. He had been worried that he too might be picked up, since he assisted me at the operation. He had rung through to the flat several times a day, asking if there was any news about me. Brunke too had been afraid of being implicated in my case. I telephoned them both that same evening and told them briefly that I was back home, and would resume duty the following morning. There was no need for them to spend another night of anxiety.

Ruth and I clinked glasses. We drank to my return, and to happier days. There was a ring at the front door. Ruth went white. I too started, but quickly got a hold on myself. "Don't worry, they're not picking me up again," I said in a brittle voice. I opened the door, and had the surprise of my life.

Outside stood Lola, with a wan smile on her face. "I must have just a few words with you, Doctor," she said, stripping off her summer coat. She greeted Ruth without any embarrassment, dropped into a chair, and smiled at me. She had grown older during the past six months. There were little lines about her eyes and her mouth. Her long titian hair had been sacrificed to the latest Western fashion in hair-styles.

I was so dumbfounded by her unexpected visit to my flat that I omitted to put a glass before her. She did not mind, but picked up mine, drained it at one long gulp, put it down again, and regarded me with a provocative smile. "You're not as well shaved as usual, Doctor," she said. "But otherwise you seem none the worse for your detention."

She knew . . . ?

"It wasn't easy to get you out, you know. The fat man was quite sad when he had to let you go. He said he had just found a splendid trail."

I stared at her speechless. "You came here on my account?"

She picked up my packet of cigarettes from the table, lit one, and enveloped herself in a blue cloud. She loved letting the cigarette smoke trickle out of her mouth without blowing it away. "The news that the surgeon who operated on Werther had been arrested spread among informed circles in Berlin this morning. I've good friends among the State Security Service, and so I happened to hear about the affair. When I found out that you were the unfortunate surgeon I went straight to the Director of the Service. He had some misgivings himself about the political advisability of arresting a surgeon on largely unsupported suspicion at the present moment. The increasing shortage of doctors is causing a great many headaches in Berlin, and an arrest like yours might have intensified a sense of insecurity among the medical profession. The first telephone reports from here, however, had made the Director decide not to interfere straight away, but to await the outcome of the investigations. Pour me out a little more Tokay, Doctor." After a hearty gulp she continued.

"To begin with, he was reluctant to be influenced by me. But when I told him that, if you were really out to murder important public figures, I ought to have been your first victim he began to prick up his ears. I told him how you had patched me up last January, and how easy it would have been for you to liquidate me without arousing suspicion. Yes, dear Doctor, that's the kind of language one has to use to these people. I then told him a lot about you, and about my impressions of your hospital. I noticed that he was glad to talk to someone who knew you personally. He immediately called several officers in for a conference and sent me out to wait in his anteroom. They reached a decision very quickly: one of their men was instructed to drive over and form his own impression of the state of the investigations. Unless there was very strong evidence against you, you were to be released at once. I was given permission to accompany him as a witness for the defence. Well, and that's how I'm here. And what's more, you're here too, Doctor."

Lola glanced at her watch. "I've got a quarter of an hour left. We've got to drive back to Berlin to-night. I used the time which my companion had to spend with the officials for a stroll through the town, and got your new address from the hospital. You've got a very nice flat here."

Ruth put another bottle of wine on the table. "My husband has told me a lot about you, Frau Oehmichen," she said. It was the first opportunity she had of saying anything.

Lola laughed, and roguishly wagged her finger at me. "Have you told her everything, dear Doctor? You ought to know that I was in love with your husband once. Yes, really; he looked after me so well at the hospital. But that's past history. I can talk about it now. Look at him—he's quite surprised. You see, I never told him."

I busied myself with the bottle to hide my embarrassment. But Lola was already continuing: "Everything has turned out different. At that time I still regarded everything as a game—my life in this country, my marriage to Under-Secretary of State Oehmichen, my luxurious home. Then the game began to bore me. I believed that I could simply put down the ball one day and say: 'I don't want to play any more.' That was how I felt on returning from hospital. I wanted to hand the ball back. The game had ceased to amuse me. The fact that my husband was continually reproaching me, that he had me secretly watched—all that I considered purely personal spite. A jealous husband will resort to the oddest measures. But then I discovered that my husband was not just motivated by jealousy. He had been given to understand that he must keep a watchful eye on me. The authorities were afraid that I might be in touch with circles hostile to our Republic.

"But presumably he failed to meet the wishes of his superiors in the way they wanted him to. People were beginning to withdraw from him. He was being cold-shouldered. I felt that the Party was putting him under pressure. When he got home at night he would be depressed and downhearted. It was then that I realized that his destiny was linked with mine. He would have been kicked out if, for the sake of argument, I had gone over to the West. Even when he had married me he had aroused suspicions among his comrades. In fact, in a manner of speaking, he had made a sacrifice for me. If I had done what at the time I felt like doing I should have brought disaster down on him. From then onwards I have stuck by him. I have given up my career as a dancer, and I have ceased to be an independent human being. I have been nothing but my husband's wife."

She lit another cigarette and exhaled the smoke. "But it was too late. The State Security Service were watching us. Not only me, but my husband as well. We had to withdraw entirely from our friends. Every morning, when my husband left for his office, I was afraid he would be back within an hour, or else not be back at all. Dismissal on the spot was quite on the cards. But equally possible too was his arrest. They were digging about in our past—in his as well as in mine. Then one evening in June, quite out of the blue, a high official of the State Security Service came to see us in our home. We had a long conversation with him. It ended with our rehabilitation. In fact, we were suddenly on good terms with the Security Service. I don't want to go into the conditions which were tied to this, but our position changed abruptly. Anyway, you were able to see for yourself to-day how great my influence has become."

We drank in silence. "All this I could only tell you in your own flat," Lola continued. "And now you'd better forget it all again

218

quickly. But don't forget me. I should like to remain friends with you, Doctor—and also with your wife."

Again she glanced at her watch. "It's time I went. And good luck to both of you!"

Ruth squeezed her hand firmly. The two women had really become friends in this short time.

11

At the hospital I was met everywhere with sighs of relief. No one asked any questions; everyone acted as if I had not been absent even for an hour. Interrogation and arrest are not things one talks about. But I felt that all their sympathies had been with me in my troubles. After the morning round Hansen followed me to my office. He made sure we were alone, closed the window, and said:

"That was a close shave you had, Herr Oberarzt. It was very foolish of you to turn down my help as you did a few days ago when I advised you to improve your relations with the Party. If I were the kind of person who is easily offended you might have spent a few more weeks at the place you were yesterday. But I'm not vindictive. I did everything I could to see you were released."

I eyed him suspiciously. Hansen my benefactor? "You did everything you could to get me released?"

"A police medical officer has various opportunities," he said significantly. "I succeeded in convincing them of your innocence."

I probably should have believed him if Lola had not visited us the night before. As it was, I could not quite suppress a slight sneer in my voice as I asked him: "And how did you manage to do that, Hansen?"

He became uncertain. "I am not allowed to mention details, Herr Oberarzt. Just rejoice in the fact that you're back with us. But I shan't be able to do the same for you again. Now it's up to you to insure yourself against suspicion. I've offered you my help in doing so already."

I told him I would think it over, and let him go. I did not believe a word of Hansen's story. But he was right on one point: I must cover myself better in future. My personal file with the State Security Service had swollen considerably. The least careless move, and they would bring up those voluminous interrogation protocols. I did not even have to be careless. Bad luck would be quite enough—as with Comrade Werther's death.

The time had come to make my decision. Either insurance—and that meant joining the Party, active co-operation, and close identification with the regime—or else I must choose the road which Reger, Busch, and Reinfeld had taken before me. The one decision was as difficult as the other.

Meanwhile there was something else to occupy my attention. I had to operate. In the lunch-hour I drove over to the Fortschritt factory to hold my surgery. Sister Suzanne told me the chief accountant was anxious to see me. He was worried about my car. The sum of DM 10,500, earmarked for the purchase of my vehicle, had to be drawn by the factory that week, or else it would lapse. I immediately picked up the chief accountant's telephone and rang up the State-owned car distributors to find out when my new car would come through. The man at the other end looked at his waiting-list and told me my name was a good way down from the top. The shop would be unable to keep to its promised delivery date of three weeks. I postponed the beginning of my surgery hour and went to see the manager of the car shop in person. He solemnly promised to give me every priority as a doctor, but was unable to quote a definite date. The motor works in Eisenach, he explained, had got behind schedule with its production programme.

I had no sooner started my surgery than the telephone rang. It was the manager of the car shop. To-morrow, he told me, three vehicles could be collected from Eisenach. But he had only two drivers. If I could arrange to go to Eisenach with them I could have the third car.

Strictly speaking, I had a hospital department to run. But I had been kept from doing so by the State Security Service for the past three days. Why shouldn't someone stand in for me for one more day? I told the manager I would come.

12

Buying a motor-car in East Germany is an adventure in itself. I asked Ruth to come to Eisenach with me. Shortly before six in the morning we met the two drivers of the State-owned car shop at the central railway station. Our two companions were old hands at the game. Before the train drew into Eisenach one of them explained the drill to us. "With us on this train are quite a lot of would-be purchasers from other towns. But outside the station there are only three taxis. The man who gets a taxi and arrives first at the factory can pick his car. The later arrivals have to take what's left. Now I'll get the taxi and keep it: you and your wife just take your time, and I'll see you outside the station."

The train was still moving when our man leapt out on to the platform and streaked away like a sprinter. He was not the only one. Quite a number of respectable-looking gentlemen were suddenly tearing down the platform, purple in the face, ties trailing behind them. Our man won the race. He was keeping back the first taxi when we emerged from the station. We drove to the office building of the motor works in the city centre. From there we drove out to the factory on the outskirts at the maximum permitted speed. The modern factory buildings were situated behind enormous black dumps of coal belonging to the State-owned coal retail organization. We wound along a narrow track between mountains of coke and coal.

We were in fact in very good time. About eighty cars were lined up in rows in the factory square, waiting to be collected. The choice of colour was not very great. The majority of the cars were blue, since the factory produced cars of only one colour for five days and then switched to a new colour series. Right at the back stood three two-tone models which appealed to Ruth. There was not much time for consideration. Look—get in—start up the engine—make up your mind.

I did not like the sound of the first engine. The second one

221

sounded better. "Oi!" one of the workers shouted across to me. "Don't you keep the engine running so long. The petrol in the tank is only just enough to get you to the pump across the road."

There was no such thing as a trial run. We decided on the two-tone model with the healthiest engine noise. Workmen pulled it out for us from the phalanx of the other cars. And there we were —the proud owners of a new car.

13

AT THE beginning of the following week the 'living corpse' returned from his holiday camp. I ran into him in Casualty in the morning. Never before had I seen the quiet young man so furious and excited. "I very nearly came back a fortnight ago," he told Kukowa and me in Frau Gummer's room. "I had the devil of a row with the camp leader. D'you remember that hot and sultry Sunday, August 28, Herr Oberarzt?"

I remembered it only to well. That was the Sunday when my patient Max Werther dropped into the coma from which he was not to waken again.

"It was the anniversary of Thälmann's death, so that Sunday was observed in the camp in a very special way. In the morning the camp leader ordered the whole camp to fall in. For an hour and a half the children were lined up in a square around the flag-pole, and were not allowed to move from the spot. The sun was beating down mercilessly. Seventeen boys and girls collapsed from the heat and just fell over. Only then could I persuade the camp leader to break off the parade. But in the afternoon the whole nonsense started again. Again twelve children collapsed. I threatened to leave at once, as I could not accept the medical responsibility for this kind of thing any longer. The parade was cut short, but an hour later the camp leader insulted me in front of the assembled officials of the Free German Youth and accused me of encouraging indiscipline."

"And quite right too," Frau Gummer intervened, in her shriek-ing voice. "Ernst Thälmann and all the other peace champions went through great hardships and sufferings for our sake. Com-pared with their heroism, what does it matter if a few healthy boys and girls have to stand in the sun for an hour? Our dead heroes are entitled to this mark of respect."

I tried to pacify her. "That's quite enough, Frau Gummer. The dignity of a ceremony does not depend on its duration."

But there I seemed to have touched our Red, Red Rose on a sore spot. "Our young people must be brought up hard, Herr Oberarzt," she harangued me. "In the West the warmongers are thrusting atom bombs into the hands of the soldiers. We've got to make up by toughness for the weapons which we proudly decline. We need disciplined young people who are immune against the infiltration of decadence from the West."

What surprised me in this speech was that she pronounced without stumbling the difficult words of the Party jargon. Which was a great deal more than could be said for Paul Kranich. But the 'living corpse' went on with his story,

"I had been asked by the Central Directorate of the Free German Youth to make a written report at the end of the camp about any incidents in the medical field. In that report I specifically men-tioned those scandalous long-duration parades on the Thälmann anniversary. In accordance with regulations I handed my report in at camp headquarters, in a sealed envelope. In the evening the camp leader informed me that he had read my report, torn it up, and thrown it in the waste-paper basket. Now the top people in Berlin can whistle for my report."

"If you ask Frau Gummer very nicely," Kukowa said mockingly, "she'll write it out for you again."

"You ought to be ashamed to joke about such things, Herr Doktor," Frau Gummer said angrily. "All weakness is bad."

Kukowa switched to his solemn voice. "On this point we are in full agreement, Frau Gummer. Walter Ulbricht said on some occasion: 'Swift as greyhounds, tough as leather, hard as Krupp steel!'"

"That was Hitler," Frau Gummer corrected.

"Impossible!" Kukowa protested. "Surely, Frau Gummer, you would never champion an ideal expounded by Hitler?"

Frau Gummer regarded him steadily. "You are quite right, there, Herr Doktor."

"Nor would you want to have anything to do with the Krupp steel of the Western militarists."

"Right again, Herr Doktor."

14

A WEEK later an event occurred which no one in the whole hospital would have believed possible. One morning Frau Gummer telephoned to say that she could not come on duty because of diarrhoea. When no sickness certificate had arrived from her three days later the hospital trade-union committee sent the chairman of its social insurance sub-committee round to her flat. He found the door locked. Other tenants informed him that the door of Frau Gummer's cellar appeared to be open. On the inside of the cellar door hung the key to her flat. The trade-union official unlocked the front door and found the flat bare except for some heavy pieces of furniture. Anything portable, from cutlery to table covers, from bed-linen to sofa cushions, had vanished. The woman we had been calling our Red, Red Rose must have prepared her flight for months and carted her property to the West, or to Berlin, piecemeal. By her zealous work on the trade-union committee and her protestations of hatred for the West she had completely deceived us all.

Kukowa was a clown who enjoyed pulling the Communists' legs without ever exposing himself to their vengeance. But Rosa Gummer was the greatest actress I had ever come across. I never discovered the reasons for her flight. But if she had a reason at all that reason must have been many months old. She had acted her part so brilliantly that no one ever doubted her sincerity for a moment.

Paul Kranich was so shaken that he admitted of only two

possibilities: "Either she has been kidnapped by Western agents or she suddenly went out of her mind," he kept telling anyone who cared to listen.

Dr Hansen bore the loss of his collaborator on the trade-union committee surprisingly lightly. He did not even complain of having to do much of the work himself. However, towards me he was strikingly taciturn. He was probably sulking because I had still not fallen in with his wishes.

My chief had meanwhile returned from Egypt. I made a detailed report to him about everything that had happened in the department. We also spoke about the medical aspect of the Max Werther case, but not a word about my subsequent arrest. Professor Zöllinger inspected the pathologist's report and expressly reassured me that this was one of those rare incidents for which no surgeon can be held responsible. "There are complications against which we are powerless," he said.

15

AFTER lunch that day Hansen followed me to my office. He grimaced and said: "I am sorry to say, Herr Oberarzt, I've got bad news for you. You must promise me not to mention a word about what I am going to tell you. Just before Werther's interment the Party Regional Committee ordered a second post-mortem to be performed by a pathologist who is a part-time police surgeon. I have not seen his report, but it is believed to differ from the first autopsy report on a number of significant points. Behind your back new investigations are being conducted against you. Unfortunately, I have been unable to do anything about it this time."

A second autopsy had been mentioned to me in the course of my interrogations. I never discovered whether one had in fact been performed. But anything is possible in our country. Could I be sure that Lola had shielded me also against future disaster? I went quite cold at the thought of being arrested again. "I really see only one way out now, Herr Oberarzt," Hansen continued in an anxious voice. "You must put your name down as a candidate for Party membership. If you hesitate too long it may be too late."

I asked him if I could not become an active member of the Trade Union Federation. "You won't be doing me a favour by joining it, Herr Oberarzt," he said. "I'm going to resign from the chairmanship of our trade-union committee. In a few weeks—and this I must ask you to keep a strict secret—in a few weeks I am to take over a *Chefarzt* post. You see, this kind of career is possible only if a man comes out openly on the side of socialism."

"All right," I said. "If you'll give me a few days I'll get the necessary papers together and put my name down. I might as well do it now."

He shook my hand and laughed. "You'll never regret it, Herr Oberarzt."

I sat down behind my desk, thinking that our conversation was concluded. But he sat down in the visitor's chair and offered me a cigarette. In an easy conversational tone he asked me if I had an hour to spare in the evening. He invited me to go to the Ratskeller with him, as there were some important matters to discuss with the District Medical Officer. I tried to hedge, but he was persistent and assured me the matter was very urgent and would not brook delay. I could not think of a good excuse, and eventually accepted.

In the evening Hansen picked me up at my flat. At their regular table in the Ratskeller sat four doctors whom I knew but vaguely. Two of them were on the staff of other hospitals, one of them was with the People's Army, and the fourth was the radiologist who had taken part in the May Day parade with his elaborately decorated motor-car. The District Medical Officer and two other doctors arrived later. Hansen so managed matters that I came to sit on the District Medical Officer's right. He regarded me absent-mindedly, put a cigar between his teeth, and said: "We've had several talks, I think. Now, what were they all about?"

"About a flat," I replied.

"That's it. Have you got one meanwhile?"

"Yes, since May."

"It's coming back to me now," said the District Medical Officer. "I had a lot of trouble with it. I had quite a job fighting your case against the hyenas of the Housing Office. But then it's part of my job to take up the cudgels for my doctors."

For two hours we sat around, engaging in trivial conversation and drinking beer. Then Hansen whispered something to the District Medical Officer. Hansen rose and motioned me to come along. We left the public bar through a door leading to the lavatories. In a passage at the back Hansen opened a door to a little private room and switched on the light. A table, covered with crumpled papers and over-full ash-trays, was anything but inviting. We did not bother to sit down, but remained standing near the door.

"Comrade Dr Hansen has recommended you as a most reliable doctor," the District Medical Officer said, tapping my lapel with the hand that held his cigar. "You want to enter your name as a candidate for Party membership. Let me assure you of my support. As you know, Dr Hansen has hitherto been the only doctor at your hospital to put himself at the disposal of the Party. He has done some splendid work, and on the 1st of October will take on the directorship of a factory polyclinic. We now need a new doctor at the hospital whom I can trust. Are you prepared to co-operate closely with me?"

I knew what that meant. I also understood why Hansen had been so eager to win me over. He was to be rewarded for his loyal services by being appointed to a *Chefarzt* job, but he had to wait until a successor had been found for him. A man who enjoyed the confidence of the District Medical Officer—or, stripped of the pompous Party phraseology—a spy.

"Yes," I said. "I'll take on the job."

The District Medical Officer was pleased. He invited me to come and see him at his regular table as often as I could in future. This concluded our first conversation. On the way home Hansen added that I could now expect to get a *Chefarzt* post shortly. At any rate, I had taken the first step towards a great career.

Ruth was still up when I got home. "The time has come," I said to her. "We'll go to the West."

Part Six

1

Beads of sweat stood on my forehead as we approached the control point. Ruth was fanning herself with a handkerchief. On the open road the draught through the car windows had been enough to cool us. But now that I had to slow down we were feeling almost unbearably hot.

I was wearing two suits, three shirts, and on top of everything a summer coat. Ruth was wearing three dresses and a light overcoat. I had turned up the legs of my inner pair of trousers as far as the knee and secured them with safety-pins. The jacket of the second suit was on the back seat of the car. The pounding of our hearts made us realize that our sweating was not only because of the heat.

The sentry saluted and stepped up to the car door. I handed him our identity cards. "Warm day, Herr Doktor," he said unsuspectingly. "Have a good time in Berlin." He waved us on.

I parked the car at the Alexanderplatz station. My jacket and overcoat pockets were stuffed full of jewellery and silver cutlery, and in my briefcase I carried a number of important medical books. Ruth was carrying a small shopping bag; in it, wrapped in towels, were cut-glass tumblers and vases. My long, thick woollen socks were stuffed full of banknotes. On my back, between vest and shirt, I wore my professional documents—certificates, degrees, and diplomas. Like that we boarded the next S-Bahn train for Charlottenburg.

Friedrichstrasse station! Policemen lined the edge of the platform. They were inspecting some of the compartments. One of them stared in through the window. I did not flinch under his gaze. The beads of sweat which collected on my forehead ran down my cheeks and dripped off my chin like tears. The policeman did not seem to notice anything out of the ordinary. He moved on sullenly. Another policeman ran past the window, stopped for a moment, glanced in, and ran on. The compartment was full of people looking bored. Nobody was reading a paper.

Why wasn't the train leaving? Why had the electric clock stopped? Surely we must have been in the station for at least three minutes? But the big hand of the clock was still on the same minute. My eyes hung on the clock hand. "Move," I implored it. "For God's sake move." Again a man in uniform strode along the edge of the platform. During the instant that he had diverted my attention the clock hand had jerked to the next minute.

"Friedrichstrasse—the last stop in the democratic sector," a woman's voice called over the loudspeaker. As if anybody could have failed to notice it! After a long pause the voice resumed: "All aboard, please. The train's leaving."

With a jerk we moved off. Above the clank and rattle of the carriage I could hear Ruth releasing her breath. The next stop was in the Western sector.

I had not notified Dr Günther Ritter. But I assumed that, since this was Saturday afternoon, I should find him at home. In case I missed him, I had made a mental note of the addresses of several other friends on whom we might call.

My assumption proved correct. The whole Ritter family were sunbathing on the balcony of their smart new flat in the Hansa district. I had not been in touch with Ritter since I rang him up from the Zoo station last spring, when I had been in Berlin for the Trade Union Federation meeting, but he could not have received us more cordially.

"You can stay here as long as you like," he said.

I glanced at my watch. "Only half an hour," I replied. "Then we go back to our car, and will come back again later."

He had thought we had come to stay in the West there and then. But we were not in that much of a hurry. We had time to bring a few small valuables across first. I had learned a lot from Frau Gummer. We undressed in the Ritters' bedroom. We left behind one of my suits, two dresses, some underwear of Ruth's, two shirts, my socks, and my shoes. I had brought along with me a pair of plimsolls to wear on the return journey. The main thing was that my documents, our jewellery, and a few other valuables were safe.

I got Ritter to show me the latest medical journals. True enough, we can subscribe to West German medical journals through the State-owned book trade, but they are not delivered to us in East Germany until they are six weeks old. This delay is not due to any organizational muddle, but is intentional. The periodicals are being held back to make sure the vacant positions advertised in the journals are no longer available when the journals are distributed. The authorities are afraid that our doctors might apply for vacant posts in the West.

In the latest issue of one of the magazines I found a post as a registrar which appealed to me. I could not expect to walk straight into an *Oberarzt* vacancy in a West German hospital. There and then, in Ritter's flat, I wrote my application and posted it.

We returned by S-Bahn to the Alexanderplatz and got into the car. During our drive Ruth filled our pockets with various small things which we had had to leave behind in the car before our first trip across the sector boundary. Any such repacking operation at the kerbside would have aroused suspicion. I drove on to another car-park, since prolonged parking in the same spot, getting out of the car twice with small pieces of luggage and returning empty-handed, might have been noticed by any observers.

Late in the evening we returned from our second trip across the border. We had completed the first phase of a well-planned operation. Through the mild September night we drove back home along the autobahn and then over secondary roads. We decided that in future we should repeat these expeditions whenever I was off duty over the weekend—in other words, every fortnight.

2

A$_T$ THE hospital I was now on my best behaviour. During scrubbing-up on Monday morning, when the other doctors spoke enthusiastically about the weekend television programmes from West Germany, I remained silent. To Kukowa's question as to what I had thought of a certain programme I replied coldly that I no longer watched West German transmissions. I am sure they did not believe me, but they probably thought that after my recent arrest I was being extra careful.

Regularly twice a week I drove out to the small district hospital for whose surgical department I continued to be ultimately responsible. Since we were now sending only post-operative cases there, at least one of the four housemen had become redundant. I saw to it that Dieter Thorn, the young man with the freckles, was transferred to our hospital and put in charge of Hansen's ward. I was now the only qualified specialist—or what in England would be called a consultant—in my four wards. Kukowa was not due to sit for his specialist's examination for several months yet. The housemen—Warberg, Ellen Tschauner, and Thorn—were not yet allowed to operate independently.

What was to happen in a few weeks' time? Conditions were no better in the other wards of the hospital. We had hardly any specialists left. Professor Zöllinger, who until the summer had spent most of his time on scientific research, was now compelled more and more often to operate himself. I determined to look out for a specialist to succeed me when I left.

On Tuesday of the following week we started preparing for our next trip to Berlin. Ruth was responsible for choosing what was to be taken. My job was to make the things into small packages which could be stowed away unobtrusively in our pockets.

Ruth had an elder brother living in West Germany. At regular intervals we now began sending him parcels filled with things which we did not want to take with us to Berlin. We also dug out the addresses of various distant relations to whom we might send packages of this kind.

Parcels for West Germany are only rarely opened nowadays. As a rule they are merely examined before X-ray screens. I therefore chose only articles which would not cast a suspicious X-ray shadow. 'Radiologically tested contraband' was the term coined by Ruth.

All parcels sent from our country to West Germany must be registered at the post-office counter, with the full name and address of the sender. Moreover, the sender must show his identity card. We therefore spread our postings over as long intervals as possible, and used as many different addresses as we could think of. Needless to say, we could not write to the addressees to explain the purpose of our parcels. Thus it happened that a distant cousin, an elderly lady living in the south of Germany, wrote us a touching letter, imploring us not to spend our hard-earned money on buying pillow-slips for her. Out of gratitude she sent us two pounds of flour and two pounds of sugar because, several years previously, someone had told her that we were very short of these foodstuffs.

On Friday night, after it had got dark, I loaded up our car for our second trip to Berlin. We were not leaving till noon, but if we had loaded up in daylight it would have aroused suspicion among the neighbours. While I was busy with the car in the garage, Ruth came down with bad news. On our first trip a fortnight ago we had left Angelica with an old couple who lived on the ground floor. They were very fond of children, and had promised Ruth to look after our daughter any time we wanted to go out anywhere by ourselves. We had counted on this arrangement.

Now it turned out that these elderly folk, who normally never went out, had been asked to a relation's birthday party for this Saturday. I decided that we should have to take Angelica with us. I did not want to waste a fortnight before our next trip.

It was only when we were on our way that we began to think of the risks of having Angelica with us. A family travelling with a child is apt to be suspected of escape by the frontier police. The sentry at the control point outside the city eyed us closely when he saw the child on my wife's lap. To forestall any question I told him that I had to have my daughter examined by a colleague at the Charité Hospital. She was suffering from a disease whose cause I had been unable to establish. He nodded, and raised the barrier.

We did not want to run this risk again at the sector boundary. We therefore decided on another plan. I parked the car in a side street near the city centre and described a route to Ruth by which she could walk across the sector boundary with her shopping bag. I took Angelica by the hand and chose another crossing-point. We were to meet in Ritter's flat.

Although I knew Berlin well, I had made a mistake in the street when I chose to park. The distance to the sector boundary was rather more than I had expected. We were strolling slowly through the deserted streets. Angelica at my side had to take three steps to every one of mine. Now and again I would pick her up and carry her for a while so that we should make better progress, but the silver cutlery in my jacket pocket hurt her. Also I was getting too hot in my two suits and overcoat. In my briefcase this time I carried heavy and potentially suspicious valuables—my camera, and a transistor radio. We had put Angelica into three sets of underwear and three little dresses.

The nearer we got to the sector boundary the more tired and irritable the child became. She tugged at her dresses, which were becoming uncomfortable, and started to cry. I suffered all the tortures the devil had invented for young fathers. Fortunately, I remembered the story of Little Red Riding Hood—Angelica's favourite fairy-tale. I had told it to her so often that she could complete every sentence I started.

In my despair I began: "Once upon a time there was a little girl and her name was . . ."

"Ickle Wed Widing Hood," Angelica finished, and again strode out bravely.

We were crossing the last side street before the sector boundary. Leaning against a lamp-post at the corner was a man of about forty. He was watching us. Men hanging about idly near the sector boundary are not, as a rule, just innocent loungers. It is their job to keep an eye on people crossing the border, and they are usually more feared than the uniformed sentries at the crossing-points.

". . . and take this little basket to your Granny. Now what shall we have in the little basket?"

Angelica eagerly started to list its contents: "Butter, eggs, bacon, meat, cheese, butter . . ."

"We've had butter."

At that point the man at the corner joined in: "You forgot the chocolate."

Angelica, unfortunately, has a weakness for strange men. "Cocolat," she crowed delightedly. "Lots and lots of cocolat."

"And so Little Red Riding Hood went off into the . . ."

". . . big wood."

"And there she met the . . ."

". . . big bad wolf."

The stranger had detached himself from his lamp-post and was strolling along with us. "Bright little girl you've got," he said to me.

I should have preferred to ignore him, but that might have been dangerous. "Yes," I said. "We're going to see her grandmother."

"And are you going to take your Granny butter, and bacon and eggs?" He turned to Angelica again.

She giggled. "Butter and eggs and bacon and cocolat." I could feel the sweat running down the back of my neck and into my collar. Taking food from the Eastern sector into the West is strictly forbidden. A small gesture from the secret policeman to the frontier guard, and my pockets would be searched. . . . Keep calm. Carry on with the story.

"And then Little Red Riding Hood asked: 'Granny, why have you such . . .'

". . . a big mouth?"

"The better to . . ."

"Eat you with."

Angelica archly turned to the stranger to let him into a secret which, so it seemed to her, he could not possibly know yet: "She's the big bad wolf."

We had reached the sentry. He was standing in the middle of

the road, bored. I intercepted a surreptitious glance he exchanged with the stranger. Did it mean that I was to be searched? With trembling lips, I continued: "And then Little Red Riding Hood said . . ."

"Wrong!' Angelica was triumphant. "Then the big bad wolf swallowed Ickle Wed Widing Hood."

The stranger, who had dropped a couple of paces behind us, laughed noisily. "A delightful child! Give your Granny my regards!"

The corner of the bombed-site was the sector boundary. Five more steps for me—fifteen more for Angelica. The sentry could still stop us. Two more steps. One more. We were safe.

3

THAT same Saturday Hansen was made *Chefarzt* of a factory polyclinic. It belonged to a large undertaking employing 15,000 workers, and was subdivided into departments for general medicine, surgery, ENT (ear, nose, and throat), and gynaecology. The specialists of all these departments were placed under Hansen's command. It was a colossal leap for the junior doctor who had earned his superiors' repeated reprimands for laziness, unreliability, and inadequate professional knowledge—straight to the rank of *Chefarzt* with a personal contract.

A personal contract is a much-coveted thing in East Germany because it provides for more generous terms of salary than the tight framework of the customary collective contract. Personal contracts are concluded only with important doctors of *Chefarzt* rank.

I now showed my face fairly frequently at the District Medical Officer's regular table in the Ratskeller. I did not enjoy myself there. It was all anecdotes and dreary stories, or at best boring medical shop. Now and then there would be some cursing of the

West or of our own bureaucracy, which, up to a certain point, it was legitimate to expose to ridicule. But by far the most important occupation was beer-drinking. Only occasionally did the District Medical Officer question his stooges about things he wished to know.

"You've got an assistant by the name of Kukowa." He turned to me abruptly. "A somewhat inscrutable type, isn't he?"

"A great clown," I said, "but politically most reliable. Moreover, an excellent surgeon. He's sitting for the specialist's examination some time in the winter."

The District Medical Officer regarded me severely. "You should be more careful with political judgments. So far he has offered no evidence of his reliability. But no doubt you talk to him often when there are no other witnesses about. On those occasions does he still display an unambiguous attitude?"

"Absolutely unambiguous," I assured him. I did not even have to lie to him.

"Look here, you'd be doing me a great favour if you tried to work on him a little, persuade him to apply for Party membership. What's more, you'd be doing yourself some good, since he could become your successor. I've already got my eye on a *Chefarzt* post for you."

I left the Ratskeller early, as I had some more packages to make up for our next trip to Berlin.

4

THIS trip was under an inauspicious star. The elderly couple were again unable to look after Angelica. I therefore asked Ruth to stay behind with her and drove off alone. To make matters worse, Ritter wrote to me at the last moment that his grandmother in Friedenau had died. This was our code against the contingency that he would not be at home on a date we had arranged.

He had written down several addresses for me, where I could go in just that event. The code word Friedenau was a clue to one of those addresses. It meant that there someone was certain to be at home. This time I had a leather suitcase full of clothes and underwear. It probably was a little foolhardy to pack so much in one case, but the easy success of our first two trips had made me bolder.

At Friedrichstrasse station I had to change. The trains for Friedenau left from a low-level platform. On the stairs stood a civilian, eyeing my case. "Criminal police. Will you please come with me?" He took me to a little room off the staircase. Two uniformed policemen inspected my identity papers and asked where I was going. I was so stunned that I could not think of an excuse. I had to open my case. The policemen stared at the hoard of clothing and demanded an explanation.

"We've been asked to a wedding," I said. "My wife's gone on ahead and is helping with the preparations. I'm bringing some of her things along." I must have said this so convincingly that they let me go. I was even allowed to take the case with me into the Western sector.

On my way back I called on Uncle Theodore. This was the first occasion that I had the time to see him in his flat near the sector boundary.

"Have you gone entirely crackers?" he burst out. "Why run this appalling risk at the border? And besides, what can you take across in a briefcase? It's just not worth the effort. Why don't you ask an adult before you go in for that kind of lark? Didn't I tell you last spring that I would help you when the time came?"

Uncle Theodore proved to be a real expert. His first question was whether my colleague Dr Ritter in West Berlin had a car. When I told him he had Uncle Theodore considered the main problem solved. Everything else he would organize himself. He left me alone for half an hour and went to have a word with another tenant in the same block, a man named Risse, who owned a car and had helped several fugitives before. He was most willing to help us. The next Saturday but one, the last Saturday in October, was chosen for our first new-style transport operation. Since I could not be sure that my rota would not be changed before then, we arranged that three days in advance I would send Uncle Theodore a postcard containing the times for both phases of the operation.

Back home we packed cases and made up large parcels. At the beginning of the week I was able to judge how late I should have to stay at the hospital the following Saturday. I sent Uncle Theodore a postcard: "Gerald has his birthday next Saturday. We've been asked round to tea at four o'clock and expect to be back home by nine. Best regards."

With a full boot, we drove off about noon on Saturday, and shortly before four o'clock reached a patch of wood about six miles our side of Berlin. We had frequently passed it before. But this time we turned into the small track which ran through the forest, and pulled up behind the first bend. We did not have to wait long before another car, with a Berlin number-plate, turned into the track and came to a halt behind ours. 'Tea at four o'clock' meant a rendezvous in the wood at the time indicated. Herr Risse got out of his car and helped us transfer our cases from our boot to his. We worked fast, wasting no words. After barely two minutes we drove off. On the far side of the wood the track ran into a secondary road which led back to the main road. By different routes we approached different control points. For the first time we had no fear at all, since we had not the smallest package with us, and we each wore no more than our normal clothes. Risse pulled up outside his front door a few minutes after us. Berlin cars are stopped very rarely at the control points outside the city. In the event of being stopped nevertheless, and made to open the cases, Risse had been ready to say he was returning from his holiday.

We deposited the cases and parcels in Uncle Theodore's cellar. Then we climbed the stairs to his flat. He winked at us slyly and told us he had spoken to Ritter the night before. Dr Ritter would be waiting in his car at the first street corner in the Western sector at nine o'clock sharp—that had been the meaning of the second time indication in our coded message. From an upstairs window we spent a long time studying the path that would take us and our cases to safety later that evening. It was not a proper path, but merely a rubble-strewn way through a bombed-site. I carefully impressed all the details on my mind, so I should not lose my way in the dark.

Uncle Theodore was explaining: "Roughly in front of my cellar window you cross the street. On the far side you keep left of that elder bush, skirt that fallen concrete post, and then follow what's left of the footings of that ruin over there. The wall gives you cover from the right. From the left you are screened for most of your way by those shrubs. When you get to the end of the footings you'll see a puddle which even in summer doesn't dry up. You can circumnavigate it from the left provided you push some branches out of the way. After that you've merely got to look out for some pieces of masonry lying on the ground. When you've reached that road over there you're in the Western sector. You can cross it quite calmly, as it is hidden from the sentry's view. Fifty yards behind that wrecked wall that's still standing you'll find Dr Ritter's car."

While we were descending to the cellar shortly before nine in the evening Uncle Theodore once more explained the posting of the frontier patrols. The sentry to our right was about a hundred yards away, and, because of a bend in the road, would not get much of a view of me. Only when he came right up to the cross-roads could he see about five yards of my proposed route. I therefore had to wait until he moved away from the cross-roads. The sentry to my left, at about the same distance, had a somewhat better view of my route, but on the other hand he had a longer beat to cover, and, when he was at the far end of it, could not see our bombed-site.

Ruth and I took up position in Uncle Theodore's cellar. The two heavy cases were standing one on each side of me, ready for me to snatch them up. Ruth was standing by the two less heavy parcels. Meanwhile Uncle Theodore was taking his evening stroll out in the street. We watched him over the short stretch of street we could overlook. He passed us several times, but we waited in vain for the prearranged signal. At last, after a long wait, he pulled his handkerchief from his pocket and went through the motions of blowing his nose. That was our signal. It meant: 'Forward at the double!' At the street corner Uncle Theodore nodded to us reassuringly as we panted past him as fast as our loads permitted. Elder bush—fallen concrete pillar—wrecked wall—everything went well. Now came the puddle, then the large chunks of masonry on the ground, clearly visible under the dim light of a street lamp. We were across. Ritter stowed our luggage away in his car and gave us a lift for a short distance along the sector boundary. He had heard from the West German hospital that I had been accepted for the post I had applied for. That had been four weeks ago. Now he had received a second letter from the Director, asking when I might be expected to arrive.

"I'm still looking for a successor," I said. "Write and ask him to wait a few more weeks."

"You're always so terribly correct," Ritter remarked. "Think of yourself, not of your successor."

We recrossed the border on foot, at a big cross-roads some five hundred yards beyond our escape route. The operation had been successful.

5

LIFE was becoming uncomfortable in our empty flat. After the first removal operation under Uncle Theodore's management we had to lock up the bedroom because all that was left on the beds were woollen blankets and there were huge yawning gaps in our linen cupboard. Since our return from the Baltic Ruth had had a charwoman three times a week. Now she was no longer allowed into the bedroom. We told her that Angelica had now reached the age when she would pull out drawers and get at such things as scent and lipstick, so we were keeping the bedroom locked. The absence of glasses and our better dinner service we explained with the story that my wife had slipped and dropped a whole trayful of things. As for our brocade table-runner, now safely in

West Berlin, we explained that Angelica had upset a bottle of ink over it, and it was now with the cleaners. A little picture, no longer in its place on the wall, had fallen down and was being reframed. As for two missing sofa cushions, we could not think of any explanation, and just hoped the charwoman would not notice.

Unfortunately, now that the evenings were drawing in, we were being invited out more often. We continually invented new excuses to avoid accepting, since we should not have been able to return the invitations. Friends who called on us unannounced were not allowed into the flat. At the front door we told them that we had the painters in, and that the place was in a mess. Then we would quickly grab our coats and carry our visitors off to a near-by restaurant.

Hansen was getting more importunate than ever. In the past we had never met outside duty hours, as he spent most of his evenings and into the nights drinking in bars. Since he had been made a *Chefarzt*, however, he had developed a penchant for domesticity and social standing. He repeatedly asked us over to his flat, and when we kept declining he wanted to visit us. Once he arrived unexpectedly, but fortunately it was a Saturday when we were in Berlin. He pushed a note through the letter-box, regretting that he had not found us in.

It was now mid-November. We had salvaged more of our property than we had ever dared hope. It was high time for us to follow. The danger of our escape preparations being discovered was increasing from day to day.

My bank account had shrunk to a small sum. Every week we had sent two packages to relations in West Germany. If there had been inspection of bank accounts or of parcel post records we should certainly have been discovered. Perhaps our neighbours had noticed our frequent trips. It was even possible that the control posts outside Berlin had repeatedly noted the registration number of our car. If the People's Police had now searched our flat no excuse in the world could have saved us from a charge of attempted flight from the Republic.

But I could not go yet. We had still not found my successor. Kukowa told me that he could not take his specialist's examination before February at the earliest. To remain in our empty flat until February 1961 would have been entirely impossible. I might as well have gone to the police there and then to give myself up.

I had decided on a bold plan. Two weeks before our departure I would apply for an interzonal pass and enter the Federal Republic legally. Ruth thought it was a crazy idea, but I was sold on it. It was to be my final revenge against a State which treated its citizens like prisoners. If a Japanese wants to go to Brazil, and already has a contract of employment there, he simply applies for an entry visa and sets out with all his personal chattels. If a German finds a job in Japan he can go there and take with him whatever he wishes. But if a German has found a new post in West Germany he is compelled to escape through night and darkness, and if he gets caught he is imprisoned for a year or two. I wanted to travel to the other Germany with at least a legal exit paper in my pocket. If I was denied it—very well, I could always go to West Berlin illegally.

November drew to its end without the problem of my successor being any nearer solution. I had told the District Medical Officer at one of our beer-drinking evenings some weeks ago that we urgently needed a qualified surgeon at our hospital. He had promised to think of me if anything turned up. But no one had applied for a post.

My situation was getting more difficult. The District Medical Officer asked what had become of my application for Party membership. Until then neither he nor Hansen had asked about it. I confessed that, largely because of a load of work, but also through forgetfulness, I had still not filled in my application form, but would do so for certain during the next few days.

"Quite all right," he said, "but I'd like to have your application by Christmas." I promised.

Early in December Professor Zöllinger had me called to his office. With him was a doctor from a small Mecklenburg hospital who had come to ask if he could have a job with us. He had had a row with his chief and his District Medical Officer, and wanted to make a fresh start elsewhere. We agreed at once that our new colleague, Dr Strelow, should join us as soon as possible. He promised to come within the next ten days. It was a real godsend. Dr Strelow had recently passed his specialist's examination. He was the man I had been looking for.

I informed Professor Zöllinger that I wished to visit some relations in West Germany over Christmas. He had no objections, and gave me two weeks' leave.

I left my chief's office and drove straight home, collected the necessary personal documents, and applied at the People's Police for an interzonal pass. I put down that I wished to travel by car. The policewoman who dealt with me advised me to come back in ten days to find out if the pass had been granted.

6

THE Association of Medical Practitioners was giving a doctors' ball. By mere chance I was able to get hold of two tickets—a success which merely worried Ruth, because our best clothes were now in West Berlin. Nevertheless, we decided to go. We just could not bear the evenings in our naked flat any longer. The empty wardrobes, the bare shelves and table-tops—everything reminded us of our imminent flight. We needed a change of scene and the company of other people. So we went off to meet the medical profession, which for once had decided to make merry.

That evening has become one of my saddest memories of East Germany. There was our town's professional élite, badly ruffled and knocked about by the Red gale, but desperately clinging to long dead and decayed traditions. The ballroom seemed to me like an island on which a handful of shipwrecked people had sought safety. But the danger from without had not welded them in a community of interests—on the contrary, it had split them up into classes and cliques. Between the separate tables invisible barriers had been erected which nobody could break down. Ruth and I had been conducted to the table of salaried specialists. In the hierarchy of the medical profession these occupied the second lowest grade. Below them were only the junior hospital doctors who had not yet passed their specialist's examination. In the next higher grade were the heads of small hospitals, and above them the professors of the big clinics. The top layer—in striking contrast to conditions in other countries—was represented by the independent medical practitioners. They enjoyed the greatest respect and received the biggest incomes. The reason for this is simply that they are a vanishing race. Independent general practitioners, the backbone of the medical services in most other countries, are no longer licensed to open practices—apart from very few exceptions. Most G.P.s in East Germany are therefore elderly people. Death and escape to the West have been decimating this group for several years. Whenever an independent G.P. has died or gone abroad his practice is converted into a State practice.

Hansen waved to us from the lesser *Chefartz* table. He was very gay, and basking in the glory of his recent social rise. He came over and asked Ruth to dance. With her impish sense of humour, she invited him to supper for the second Sunday in January. By that time we should be either in the West or else—well, we hoped it would be the West.

The secretary of the local Health Service Accountant's Office rose and tapped his glass with a spoon. He then made a speech which was spiced with the kind of humour that would barely have elicited a smile in the days when the men wore stiff wing collars and the ladies narrow wasp waists. He trotted out every possible cliché about all work and no play, about the charms of the fair sex, about letting joy be unconfined, about the noble grape and the flowing spring. His speech smelt as musty as his rarely worn dinner jacket.

Things were beginning to get noisy at the table of the 'independents.' They owed it to their position to drink Crimean champagne at DM 23 a bottle and to run up a big bill. At the *Chefartz* table most of the regulars seemed to content themselves with a cheaper German brand from the Saale and Unstruth vineyards. In this hierachy it was proper for us to remain below the *Chefarzt* level: we made do with West German or Hungarian wines.

The independent doctors were envied by everybody, but their tired and lined faces showed that they did not easily earn their high incomes. Most of them did part-time work in hospitals, industrial undertakings, or other State establishments. The older ones in particular were anxious to find subsidiary employment under the State, since this earned them an old-age pension. The daily routine of many an independent general practitioner is something like this: from eight in the morning till four in the afternoon he works at a hospital, a first-aid station, or some other State health establishment, and from six in the evening till midnight he has his surgery or visits his patients. Only by driving themselves in this way can the G.P.'s earn their high monthly incomes of DM 3000 to 4000. But, of course, it enabled them now, at this medical ball, to exchange holiday reminiscences of Bulgaria, the Russian Black Sea coast, Egypt, or even India, while we salaried specialists were circulating our more modest snaps from the Baltic beaches.

I was watching this revelry of a moribund and indeed dying profession, which still clung to its traditional social forms, with the eyes of a man who had already said good-bye to it all. There was no doubt left in my own mind as to which way our profession was going in East Germany. The type of the old family doctor had long disappeared. The independent G.P. with a long list of health insurance patients is gradually dying out. The younger generation, to which I belong, is forced to remain in hospitals and other State health institutions. The doctor of the future will be a civil servant. Politically the bulk of State-employed doctors has not yet been infected, but the Hansens are on the advance. They make the more rapid progress, and are appointed to all the key posts.

Among those of our profession whose consciences will not let them follow that road to the bitter end, a great many yet will be forced into the decision that I had taken.

Late at night the invisible barriers between the tables began to crumble. Small arguing groups formed everywhere. While Ruth was chatting with the wives of some colleagues Hansen asked me over to his table. There a Meritorious People's Doctor was holding forth. "And now I can't find anyone to buy it off me," he complained loudly. "All the bonus I got with my title is now gone.

And it really is a very nice weekend chalet—you can even see a few West German mountain-tops from the window. But it's just got that one drawback—it's just inside the prohibited three-mile belt. I never gave it a thought at first—after all, it's nearly an hour's walk from the State frontier."

"And aren't you allowed to spend weekends there?" another man asked.

"Oh, yes. Except that for every visit I need an entry permit into the three-mile prohibited zone along the frontier. I get that permit all right if I can show that I'm the owner of the house. But you don't just want to live in a place like that—you want to show it off to your friends. I'd prepared a splendid house-warming party. I'd asked twenty people—but not one of them turned up. There I was with my wife, surrounded by bottles and simmering with anger. When I got back on Monday I discovered that none of my friends had been given an entry permit. An invitation to a party was not considered sufficient reason. One's got to own a plot of land in the frontier zone oneself, or else be resident there. I don't get any fun out of spending my weekends there alone with my wife. If I want to do that I'm more comfortable in my flat. Wouldn't any of you like to buy that chalet off me?"

The others merely laughed and shook their heads.

I drifted to another group. "And why didn't you bring your charming young daughter to the ball to-night?" an elderly general practitioner was asking the head of a polyclinic.

"She's at the university in Leipzig," he replied proudly.

"At the university? Unless my memory deceives me, she didn't get permission to go to university."

"Quite right," the head of the polyclinic agreed. "She was turned down in the spring. But then I really cut up rough. 'If my daughter doesn't get permission to study in this country,' I told them, 'then I'll send her to a West German university.' That shook them. In the autumn she was admitted in spite of her bourgeois background. But then they've always assured us doctors that the children of the intelligentsia would be admitted to the universities. That's what I kept quoting at them."

I moved off again presently, for in this group the head of the

Medical Advisory Commission was trying to exploit the relaxed atmosphere to enrol new members for his Commission. Service on this Commission—which is designed to keep an eye on the activities of doctors—is both unpleasant and badly paid. Most doctors try to dodge it. I did not stop long at the next table either. There the heavy Hungarian wine had loosened the tongues of a few elderly gentlemen. "How long can things go on like this?" a white-haired veteran asked. And another added: "They've got us where they want us."

I ran into Kukowa on the edge of the dance floor. "Whenever I see doctors revelling I feel like operating, Herr Oberarzt," he groaned. "Just a little incision on their eyelids to open their eyes."

The District Medical Officer joined us and removed his cigar from his mouth. "What, talking shop?" he asked genially.

"We are discussing the latest operation techniques," Kukowa said, poker-faced.

The District Medical Officer invited us to join him in a little Russian brandy. I realized that he intended to test Kukowa, to see whether he was a suitable successor for me. Kukowa passed with flying colours. He chucked so much Communist jargon about that the District Medical Officer got quite alarmed and left us under some pretext.

After two more dances Ruth and I left. "Well, what was your impression?" Ruth asked. "How do the other doctors feel?"

I quoted my elderly colleague: "They've got us where they want us."

7

THE following Tuesday I had to inquire about my interzonal pass. It was the Tuesday before Christmas. Neither Ruth nor I had slept a wink that night. Our nerves were on edge. Never before had I felt this stifling sense of fear—not when I was held by the State Security Service nor during our adventures on the sector boundary. By now it was a matter of complete indifference whether I got my pass or not. I felt like a man who intended to cash a dud cheque, but knew the police might be waiting for him at the bank.

I had been a fool to apply for an interzonal pass. Surely they must have made inquiries about me; surely they must have looked for any indications of my preparing to skip the country? During the past few days the telephone in our flat had rung repeatedly. When we picked up the receiver there would be silence at the other end. But we could hear someone breathing. Were they trying to make sure we were still here? We had tried to be careful, but we were certain to have made quite a few suspicious moves.

I tried to picture what would happen at the police station in the morning. If the policewoman reached for the card index all would be well. I would simply have to surrender my identity papers in exchange for a temporary identity card.

If she told me the pass had not been granted I should still not be sure about the reason. Had it been refused on some bureaucratic grounds, or did they suspect us of not intending to return? In the latter case it was possible that we were being watched.

If she asked me to wait a moment it would almost certainly mean arrest. That was the trap I was afraid of.

Shortly before eight I left the house. I had arranged with Ruth to ring her by ten o'clock at the latest. If I had not rung through by then she and Angelica were to take the eleven o'clock train to Berlin—if it were not too late.

Shortly after eight I joined the queue outside the People's Police registration office. It was quite a long queue, since many people had applied for interzonal passes for the Christmas holidays. It was nearly an hour before my turn came. As I discovered subsequently, I had set up a new kind of record during this waiting period: from a new packet of *Juwel* cigarettes, with which I had set out from home, eight were missing.

I was dealt with by the same policewoman to whom I had handed my application for the pass. Without a word, I slid my identity card across the counter. Now was the moment that would decide my fate. I stared at the ugly girl. She was unconcerned, impersonal.

When she read my name she looked up. She snapped my identity card shut. "One moment, Herr Doktor," she said.

I felt myself go white.

"You'll have to see the lieutenant. This door on the left, if you please."

All the blood drained from my legs. I could not feel whether they were touching the ground or not.

"Take your identity card with you." I had forgotten about it. I thought I could see a smile on her face. But I might be wrong.

A moment later I was facing the lieutenant. I handed him my identity card and wanted to say something. But my throat was constricted.

He glanced cursorily at the identity card. His voice seemed to come from a long way off. "When did you intend to leave the German Democratic Republic?" he asked.

"To-morrow," I said. My voice sounded hoarse and unsteady.

"I'm afraid I have to disappoint you, Herr Doktor. To-morrow is out of the question."

I quite expected to find myself seized by two policemen from behind. I stood motionless.

"You see, it's like this," the lieutenant went on ponderously. "Only your wife's interzonal pass has come through. After all, it's your wife's brother you want to visit, not your own. But the Politburo issued some new directives yesterday concerning doctors. That was why I had your file looked up. In the light of these new directives it is possible now—you realize I can't make any promises—as I say, it's possible now that your application will be favourably considered. Come back first thing to-morrow morning. Walk straight through to me—no need to queue. I hope I may be able to give you a final reply then."

I thanked him and staggered out. Back in the car I lit my ninth cigarette. I had to run over the whole thing again in my head. What the lieutenant had told me sounded quite plausible. Or could it be a trap after all? Was I being kept here for another day so that my flat could be searched, my bank account inspected, and any suspicious circumstances ferreted out?

I started the engine and drove to the hospital. From my office there I telephoned Ruth and told her that everything was still in the balance.

Kukowa meanwhile had made a start on the first operation. While I was scrubbing-up, male nurse Bollmann came into the room to get some cottonwool. "Have you seen the paper, Herr Oberarzt?" he asked. "The Politburo has decreed some very considerable concessions for doctors. More private practices are to be licensed. And all sorts of other concessions."

"Oh, yes, I know about it," I replied. I did not want to confess to Bollmann that I was not a subscriber to the Party daily, the only daily in our town. He did not notice my sigh of relief. So what the lieutenant had told me was true. But some doubts persisted. Every hour or so I telephoned Ruth to ask her about some triviality or other. I did not want to disquiet her by asking outright if our flat had been searched. But the fear of it stayed with me until the evening.

I had meanwhile bought a newspaper and read the report about the Politburo's decisions. Moreover, they were the main topic of conversation in the hospital.

At home that evening I discussed the new concessions for doctors with Ruth. We were to have greater material rewards than hitherto. Perhaps I should be able to open a private practice in the near future. A *Chefarzt* post would almost certainly come my way now, thanks to my new contacts with the District Medical Officer. *Chefarzt* and a private practice on top—over in the West I could not expect anything approaching that for the next few years. Over there I had a junior hospital appointment with a modest salary. With the large number of doctors in West Germany, the starting up of a private practice must be several years away, let alone a private specialist practice as a surgeon.

"Well, that's the situation," I said to Ruth, putting down the paper. "There is still time. The greater career, the more luxurious life—these we'll find here. Over there lies uncertainty. Well, what do you think?"

She smiled at me. "I've told you a dozen times," she said, "that I will do whatever you do. I leave the decision to you."

"I have decided. We are going."

She drew me into her arms. "Thank you, Peterkin," she said.

8

AT EIGHT o'clock sharp I walked into the lieutenant's office at the police station. He flashed his snow-white teeth at me in a big smile. "You see, Herr Doktor, I was right about the tip I gave you," he said. "The passes have come through. And you can take your car. Now I shall want your identity cards."

Five minutes later the formalities were over.

I drove to the hospital. A good thing there were no traffic lights in our town! I was so elated I should have disregarded them. I rang Ruth at once. "Pack our bags; we're off to-morrow," was all I said.

I was in time to make my morning round in my ward. I had taken over my old ward again, since Ellen Tschauner came and went when she pleased.

Granny Novotny was not in pain. She was in high spirits, and hoped we should shortly discharge her. I did not think so myself, but I did not tell her so.

"May I tell you something that's nothing to do with my illness, Herr Oberarzt?" she asked shyly.

"What is it?"

"D'you remember Frau Brinkmann, Herr Oberarzt? Her husband came yesterday and brought me this chocolate. Here, have a piece. They let him out last week. The flat's gone—you know all that. But he's found an attic room in Rosa Luxemburg Street, at No. 16. Funny—same number as our ward here. And he's brought his wife home from the nursing centre. I'm so glad."

"Well, this really is good news, Granny Novotny," I said.

"Oh, yes, and Steinkopf, the master locksmith, has so far managed to hang on to his workshop," she added quickly.

I felt elated in the operating theatre. This was the last time I would be operating on that table. But only in spirit could I say good-bye to the team I had directed for so long. "This is a memorable operation, Sister Helga," I said. She looked at me incredulously. A stomach resection like many another, the patient an ordinary workman, the usual routine—what was so memorable?

During the next operation, a hernia, I repeated my remark. Everybody smiled, as Sister Helga was visibly trying to discover the memorable features of the hernia. But their smiles were born of embarrassment, for none of them knew what I meant.

During our last operation Helga asked whether this too was a memorable appendix. I bent over the operation area as if looking for special features, and announced solemnly: "Yes, Sister Helga, this is a very special appendix."

Male nurse Bollmann intervened. "This reminds me of our major when I was with the parachutists. He too announced one morning that this was a memorable day. You know, just a feeling he had. And in the evening—what d'you think happened that evening? He was so drunk he fell down the cellar stairs and broke his neck."

Kukowa sighed. "Trust a parachutist to say the tactful thing."

Out in the corridor, near his peace corner, I was intercepted by Paul Kranich. "I understand, colleague doctor, that you've received an interzonal pass," he said. "You see how well we treat our doctors? But when you're over there in the West, don't you let yourself be blinded by whipped cream and Yankee cigarettes. You're an intelligent man, colleague doctor. You'll realize how rank, rotten, and corrupt that country of capitalists and militarists really is."

In the early afternoon I drove Kukowa out to the district hospital, where he was to take my place during my absence. I introduced him to the remnant of the quartet—the three housemen—as well as to Sister Martha and the rest of the staff of the surgical department. Padereit, the administrator, was in the workshop, making wooden stands for Christmas-trees. He invited

Ruth and me to a hospital party to be held early in January. I accepted.

I next drove out to the Fortschritt factory to discuss some final arrangements with Sister Suzanne before my departure. This was not an official surgery, but Alfred Fritsche, the works militia leader, had seen my car from his little guard hut, and presently walked in. "It's the old rheumatism, Herr Doktor," he complained. "And at Christmas too."

I prescribed some pain-killing tablets for him, and asked him to come back for my first surgery in the new year. I had long ceased to enjoy this little joke: it now seemed lies and hypocrisy. But I had no choice.

I was back at the hospital in time for the afternoon round. It was to be my last. It was a painful hour, which I should prefer to expunge from my memory. I felt ashamed at doing what I had always tried to avoid. I was sneaking off, leaving patients on whom I had operated for others to look after. I stopped for quite a while at each bed. I had a little chat with every patient. But I was careful to keep my thoughts to myself: this one will do now, he can be discharged in a few days. But this one here is beyond help. Hope they'll look after him well during his last days. And the old woman in the next bed? Who can tell? Supposing she has a relapse—will Kukowa and that new man Strelow be able to manage?

I turned briefly in the doorway: "I shall be going away on leave. Doctor Kukowa will be looking after you in my absence. All the best."

I passed Frau Piesewitz in the corridor and complimented her on the beautiful glossy finish of her polished floors. She laughed, flattered, brushed a strand of hair from her face with her sleeve, and said: "That's because of the new food trolleys with rubber wheels, Herr Oberarzt. They don't mark the floor as the old ones did."

I walked with Sister Eva as far as her ward office. She had become fuller and more womanly since having her baby. She had put him in an infant crèche because she had to resume work six weeks after her confinement. Ernst Pfeifer could not keep a family on his outdoor staff wages.

Male nurse Nitschke was clearing up in Casualty. He had

become calmer and more even-tempered since he had ceased to be bullied by Frau Gummer.

I saw Professor Zöllinger in his laboratory, where he was bending over Petri dishes and Erlenmeyer flasks. He rarely told us the purpose of his experiments, and then only when they had been completed. He asked me briefly when I would be back.

"On the 3rd of January," I said, adding more softly: "Unless anything unforeseen happens."

He nodded. Did he suspect my intentions? He seemed much too engrossed in his research to want to discuss my trip with me.

I went back to my office for the last time. I did not switch on the light, but walked over to the window. In front of me, lights blazing in the windows, were the wards of the two departments. To my extreme left I saw Professor Brunke's office. He was sitting at his desk. His curtains had not been drawn. He had a lot of worries just now. His sleep-therapy ward had been closed down earlier in the month for lack of patients. The rooms were used again as general wards.

Across the yard, under the roof of the ward block, another light went on. That must be Matron Kress's room. She was looking contented again on her rounds of the wards, and her hair-style and make-up were emphatically youthful. She had found in our freckled houseman Dieter Thorn a new friend, and successor to Pütz and Scholz.

Across the yard, in his white coat, came the 'living corpse.' These were his last days at our hospital, since the District Medical Officer had made him take over a rural clinic as from January 1. He had resisted for a long time, as he had been unwilling to give up his flat, but the District Medical Officer had come out victorious in the unequal struggle.

By the door of the ward block stood Ernst Pfeifer in his blue overalls, a muffler round his neck, his hands thrust into his pockets. He had been off duty for some time. He was probably waiting for Sister Eva. I opened the window and inhaled the cool evening air. It smelt of half-burned brown coal and ash. The fine grey ash was again settling on roofs, window-sills, and the ground throughout the hospital compound, as it did every winter.

A sudden draught made me realize that the door had been

opened. Frau Möser, our common-room servant, came in and looked embarrassed. I switched on the light and fished out my wallet. "Seeing that you won't be here at Christmas, Herr Oberarzt . . ." she was stammering. I thrust a ten-mark note into her hand. She thanked me and shuffled off.

9

WHEN I got home the cases were packed. "What shall we do with the rest?" Ruth asked in despair. There was the radio, a small carpet, a stool, a folding table, and a few other things of some little value. "It would be a shame to leave it all to the Party bosses," Ruth said. I considered. We could not give any of it to our friends, since that might have aroused suspicion.

Suddenly I saw the answer. Rosa Luxemburg Street, the same number as the ward—yes, No. 16, an attic room. That should not be too difficult to find. It was dark enough to take the things down to the garage and stow them in the car. I drove across to Rosa Luxemburg Street. Panting heavily, I climbed the four flights of stairs several times, lugging the heavy pieces up with me, and putting them down in a dark corner of the landing outside the attic room. Not until I had brought up everything did I knock at the door, on which a square piece of cardboard was fixed with two drawing-pins: 'B. Brinkmann.'

A man of about sixty, with a stoop, opened the door. I asked him to close it behind him, so that his wife, who must be in bed, should not recognize my voice. "You are Herr Brinkmann?" I asked. "I've been asked to bring a few things to you. Will you please accept them as Christmas presents from a family acquainted with your story? If you really feel you must thank anybody for it, let it be Granny Novotny at the hospital."

I left him standing there, open-mouthed, and hurried down the stairs.

A long night of worry and torment followed. Had we done anything suspicious on our last day? Had the police spies got on to our tracks? The fear was to remain with us until we had left the country.

We left our cellar door unlocked. On top of our crate of potatoes I put a little package for our charwoman and a chess-board for the elderly couple on the ground floor who had looked after Angelica during our trips. I added two little notes: 'Just something to remember us by.' I likewise left the garage door unlocked, and on the garage floor I put our front-door keys. Then we drove off before the day began to dawn.

The check at the frontier was cursory. The heavy Christmas traffic kept the frontier police even busier than usual. At the barrier a uniformed man cast a last quick glance at our passes. Then he raised the barrier: "Have a good trip, Herr Doktor."